THE TURQUOISE SEA

THE TURQUOISE SEA

Hilary Wilde

CHIVERS
THORNDIKE

This Large Print book is published by BBC Audiobooks Ltd, Bath, England and by Thorndike Press®, Waterville, Maine, USA.

Published in 2006 in the U.K. by arrangement with the author.

Published in 2006 in the U.S. by arrangement with Juliet Burton Literary Agency.

U.K. Hardcover   ISBN 1–4056–3669–6 (Chivers Large Print)
U.K. Softcover   ISBN 1–4056–3670–X (Camden Large Print)
U.S. Softcover   ISBN 0–7862–8439–0 (British Favorites)

The text of this Large Print edition is unabridged.
Other aspects of the book may vary from the original edition.

Set in 16 pt. New Times Roman.

Printed in Great Britain on acid-free paper.

British Library Cataloguing in Publication Data available

Library of Congress Cataloging-in-Publication Data

Wilde, Hilary.
    The turquoise sea / by Hilary Wilde.
        p.   cm.
    "Thorndike Press large print British favorites."—T.p. verso.
    ISBN 0–7862–8439–0 (lg. print : sc : alk. paper)
    1. Governesses—Fiction. 2. Single fathers—Fiction.
    3. British—Mozambique—Fiction. 4. Mozambique—Fiction.
    5. Large type books. I. Title.
PR6072.E735T87 2006
823'.914—dc22   2005037327

CHAPTER I

Kate hurried up on deck and went to lean against the ship's rail, looking excitedly over the Indian Ocean, past the miles of sand dunes, to where the white villas and tall buildings of Lourenço Marques were slowly coming into view. This was to be her home for the next six months. She had thought 'Lourenço Marques' sounded romantic, but the name of the country—Mozambique—was even more exotic. What a difference names made, she thought, and yet how foolish it was to let them influence her. But she could not help it. She was keyed up with expectancy and could hardly wait for the ship to dock and her new life to begin.

She crossed the deck and went to the other side of the ship. Here the land was farther away, and she watched two white-sailed boats scud across the water. How beautiful it all looked. The blue sky was cloudless, and although it was still early, the sun was very hot. Would she be able to stand the heat? she wondered, and then had to laugh at her own nonsense. Surely, after a seemingly endless frosty winter in England, a little heat would not worry her?

She hurried across the ship again; to stand gazing almost hungrily at the town.

Somewhere, living in one of those houses, was a little girl called Rose. A child born of an English father and a Portuguese mother; whose father had suddenly become worried about her upbringing and had decided to engage an English nursery governess for her.

Kate was to be that nursery governess.

'Getting excited?' a friendly voice asked.

Kate turned and saw Mrs. McCormack, who had shared her cabin from England, smiling at her.

'You've got the wrong tense,' Kate said, laughing. 'I could hardly sleep all night.'

'I noticed you ate very little breakfast,' Mrs. McCormack said with mock severity.

Kate smiled at her affectionately. It was amazing how fond she had grown of Mrs. McCormack, but then she had so much cause for gratitude. In the first days, when Kate had discovered that she was not a good sailor, life had been like a nightmare, but Mrs. McCormack had been more than kind, and had nursed and mothered her. Later, when Kate was better and could join in the fun of shipboard life, Mrs. McCormack was always there when wanted, yet would tactfully vanish when she saw Kate was with a young crowd. Best of all, Mrs. McCormack had shown plainly that she liked Kate and enjoyed being with her. The truth was, of course, that Mrs. McCormack should have had a large family. She had a great heart and an unlimited capacity for loving. She badly needed several daughters and at least three sons! As it was, she had but one child—a son. Her wonderful James, about whom she was prepared to talk all day long. Yet, according to Mrs. McCormack, James had grown up to be a very independent young man and was certainly not a spoilt mother's boy. Kate sometimes wondered whether this was due to Mrs. McCormack's wise handling of her own great love for her child, or whether it was due to James's character.

Even as Kate smiled, she saw Mrs. McCormack turn to a woman standing by her side whom Kate had not noticed before, and her heart sank. It was Mrs. Kelly. Everyone on board tried to avoid her, for she was one of those women who ask awkward questions in such a way as to make it almost impossible not to answer her without being rude. Everyone disliked her for she was not only inquisitive but always criticising; only Mrs. McCormack ever had a good word to say about her.

Now Mrs. McCormack was smiling rather apologetically: 'Kate dear, Mrs. Kelly would love to hear about your new job.'

Kate repressed a small sigh but, knowing it was not Mrs. McCormack's fault, managed a smile. 'Of course, what would you like to know, Mrs. Kelly?'

Mrs. Kelly looked at her and spoke without hesitation, almost as though she had been rehearsing her questions. 'How did you obtain this post? It is most unusual for us to have a European nanny out here—they're usually black.'

'I'm not a nanny—' Kate corrected her quietly. 'I was trained as a children's nurse and have also taught in nursery schools.'

Mrs. Kelly looked at the slight young girl and sniffed. 'I understand Mr. Lister'—she spoke disdainfully—'engaged you in London?'

Kate wondered at the cross-examination, but seeing the appealing look in Mrs. McCormack's eyes, answered politely. 'That is correct. I worked for a firm of shipping agents in London and one day, my boss, Mr. Stowe, introduced me to a client of his—a Mr. Lister. Mr. Stowe told me that Mr. Lister was looking for an English girl to take charge of his daughter. Knowing that I had previously worked with children, Mr. Stowe thought I might be able to offer some advice, or tell Mr. Lister the name of the college where I was trained . . .'

Kate paused, remembering the excitement in the office, the chatter over the teacups as the girls warmed their feet by the gas fire and the thick yellow fog pressed close against the windows.

'Eventually,' Kate continued, 'Mr. Lister offered me the post and I took it.'

'You're very young to come out to a foreign land,' Mrs. Kelly said. 'How old are you?'

The abrupt question annoyed Kate. 'I am nineteen, nearly twenty.'

Mrs. Kelly looked disapproving, and almost as if she was trying to call Kate a liar as she went on: 'How can you have *trained* as a nursery school teacher, for it's a three years' course?'

'I didn't say I had . . .' Kate began indignantly, and then took a deep breath. 'I'm afraid I didn't make it plain. I said I was trained as a children's nurse. I should have said I also *worked* in a nursery school. I was starting as a trainee teacher to see if I wanted to take it up seriously, and then I was offered a good post to look after two children, so I didn't finish the training.'

'H'm. Pity to start something and not finish it.' Mrs. Kelly's eyes were sharp. 'Have you no relations to advise you?'

Kate bit her lip. Quick-tempered, although used to controlling herself, she began to feel that there were limits beyond which Mrs. Kelly should not go.

'My mother met Mr. Lister,' she said with some dignity, 'and she gave her consent before I accepted his offer.'

Mrs. McCormack interrupted hastily, as if seeing that Kate's hard-tried patience was drawing to an end. 'I can't see any reason why Kate should not come out here to work. It's a wonderful opportunity for a girl. Look, Kate dear . . .' Her hand on Kate's arm, she waved her hand towards the coast. 'Can you see that big white building? That's the Polana Hotel. You'll like it there. Very good dances—nice band.'

Mrs. Kelly blandly ignored Mrs. McCormack's well-intentioned effort to sidetrack her. 'But why has Mr. Lister suddenly decided he needs an English girl to look after his child?'

Kate sighed. If only they would both go away and leave her alone! She snatched a hasty glance at the town that could now be plainly seen. There were masses of flowers in the gardens, lines of cars speeding along the roads—big white villas. It looked a tropical town—wealthy and unusual.

'It's a long story,' Kate began hopefully, thinking it might deter Mrs. Kelly, but that hatchet-faced woman with the disapproving eyes and the pursed mouth merely nodded, so Kate had to go on. 'I understand he lost his wife when the baby was a week old.' Kate paused, remembering the look on Randel Lister's face when he told her: 'My wife only had time to say she was glad our baby had golden hair and that she would be our English rose. That was why I christened her Rose,' he had said in a carefully emotion-free voice. Now Kate looked briefly at the town sliding by and thought how very deeply Mr. Lister must have loved his wife. Mrs. Kelly coughed and Kate hurriedly remembered her.

'Mr. Lister, as perhaps you know, works for a big oil firm. They sent him to America, but the baby was delicate and he did not know what to do—luckily his mother-in-law said she would take care of the baby.'

Mrs. Kelly looked very shocked. 'He just left the child?'

'What alternative had he? After all, he has his job and the baby has thrived. Every six months Mr. Lister is in Lourenço Marques and sees her. It was only quite recently that he realised she was not a baby any longer and . . .'

'Was conscience-stricken, poor man,' Mrs. McCormack said gently.

Kate smiled at her. 'Those were his exact words. He remembered his promise to his wife—that he would bring up their child to be a little English girl.'

'His wife was English?' Mrs. Kelly rapped.

'No. Portuguese. She had a lovely name, Candida.'

'Certainly more character to it than Rose. What is he like—Mr. Lister? I have heard of him but never met him.'

Kate gripped the rail tightly. How much more must she stand? How could she snub a woman so much older than herself?

'I have only met him twice,' Kate told her, in a deliberately-controlled voice. 'It's difficult to describe him.'

That was not quite the truth. Those two meetings had etched his image on Kate's mind

7

so that, as long as she lived, she knew she would never forget him. He was tall with amazingly broad shoulders—always very well dressed. His clear grey eyes had surveyed her sombrely and had suddenly lit up into a smile that made him look years younger, as it illuminated his naturally serious face. A grave, deep voice that carried authority. He held his head with an unconscious arrogance, his dark hair was smooth. Kate had thought at once that here was a man to be respected, a man who made you feel 'safe.'

'My mother liked him very much and she is usually considered a good judge of character.'

'Is he a *nice* man, Kate?' Mrs. McCormack asked rather anxiously. To Mrs. McCormack, there were only two kinds of men. Men you could trust—and men you could not! Naturally, James came under the first heading. Now her voice showed plainly that she was wondering if the same could be said for Mr. Lister.

Kate smiled at her. Dear, funny Mrs. McCormack! All those long talks they had had about men and their ways! Mrs. McCormack had said very much the same as Kate's own mother had before her—but Mrs. McCormack had a lot of advice to offer about Portuguese men. She had said that all well-brought-up Portuguese girls were sheltered, and if a girl went unchaperoned in Portuguese East Africa—in other words, Mozambique—and

8

was free and easy, men had no respect for her.

'You forget Mr. Lister is English,' Kate said, meaning it as a gentle joke. To Mrs. McCormack, despite her name, there was only one flag in the world worth saluting, one anthem, one country. In her eyes, an Englishman was a chivalrous gentleman who could do no wrong.

But Mrs. McCormack took the remark seriously. 'I had forgotten. He should be all right.'

Mrs. Kelly gave an especially violent sniff. 'Men are all the same under the skin. I cannot understand why he suddenly decided to engage an English girl—and a young, pretty one at that. If his mother-in-law has hitherto brought up the child so successfully, why make a change now?'

Kate, hiding a smile because of Mrs. Kelly's accidental compliment, tried to explain. 'Mr. Lister said Rose was growing up to be *too* Portuguese. Not that he minded that, but he *had* promised his wife that Rose should be English, and as his future will probably be in England, he thought it time to make a change. He has arranged for a transfer to England, but it will take six months, so he decided to have an English nanny for a time.'

'And what does the grandmother say?' Mrs. Kelly demanded.

Kate stared at her. For a moment she did not know what to answer. This was an angle she had neglected to think about.

Mrs. Kelly went on, sounding quite triumphant. 'She won't be at all pleased, I'm sure. Portuguese women are possessive and jealous to a degree. I wonder, too, how you will fit into a Portuguese household.' She stared at Kate and then shrugged her shoulders. 'Well, we can only hope for the best. I presume he has guaranteed your return passage if things don't turn out well?' She waited for Kate's nod and then walked away without another word.

Kate and Mrs. McCormack watched her walking down the deck with her firm, flat-footed, almost martial tread, and then looked at one another. Kate was not sure whether to burst out laughing or express her anger.

'Poor dear,' Mrs. McCormack said quickly. 'I hope Mrs. Kelly is happier now. She has planted the seed of disquiet in your mind.' She gave Kate a shrewd glance. 'She has done that, hasn't she, dear child?'

Kate nodded miserably. 'I'm afraid I never thought of the grandmother's feelings.'

Kate felt that somehow she was at fault. She ought to have thought of the Portuguese grandmother, but she had been far more concerned with the need to win little Rose's confidence, of being her friend. It was always a problem with children—to start off on the right foot, so to speak. 'Mrs. McCormack, do you think the grandmother will be difficult? I hadn't thought of that,' she finished unhappily.

'Now, my dear child,' Mrs. McCormack's hand closed over Kate's. Her voice showing concern, annoyance with Mrs. Kelly, and distress that Kate now feared what lay ahead. 'Don't cross your bridges till they're built, my dear. She does love moaning and forecasting trouble. Don't let this influence your thoughts, Kate dear. You were so happy. All the same, I think there are a lot of things you have not thought of, dear.' Mrs. McCormack sighed a little. 'You may meet resentment, jealousy— even hostility. So much will depend on the type of woman the grandmother is. Some of my best friends are Portuguese, and I certainly would not like to generalise by calling them jealous or possessive, but . . .' She laughed a little uneasily. 'We must just wait and see, dear. They could make life difficult for you. On the other hand—' She made an obvious effort to sound more cheerful. 'On the other hand, dear child, if Mr. Lister has any sense he will have made the situation so clear that there need be no difficulties. You have got my telephone number?' she finished anxiously.

The town was now quite near and they could see people waiting on the docks. There were great cranes and derricks, trucks driving along, a railway train slowly shunting, swarms of natives watching the incoming boat.

'Yes—I have got your telephone number,' Kate said with a warm smile.

11

Mrs. McCormack looked at the girl anxiously. 'You're so very young and pretty,' she said, almost sadly. That was her second compliment that day, Kate thought quickly, but this one she welcomed for it was said with affection. 'How tall are you, Kate?' Mrs. McCormack went on. 'You are so little. Just five feet?'

Kate laughed; she was used to being teased about looking like a shrimp.

'Exactly five feet three inches.'

'I wish—' Mrs. McCormack began, and sighed. 'What's the use of wishing?' She smiled at Kate. 'You're so pretty, Kate. Don't blush, my dear, that's not a compliment but the truth. I love your hair. It shines. Could you believe that mine was once that honey-brown colour?'

Kate tried to hide her surprise, for Mrs. McCormack's hair was now a very sophisticated, smokey blue-white and beautifully groomed. How elegant she was, Kate thought. She held herself so upright, as if a poker was hidden down the back of her frock. And though she was rather plump, her clothes were so well cut that you hardly realised her size. Her biggest weakness, which she always admitted laughingly, was a passion for diamonds.

Mrs. McCormack was beginning to look flustered. 'We'll soon be there. You have promised to telephone, Kate,' she said urgently. 'I'll be worrying about you until I hear.'

Kate took the older woman's arm. 'I've promised, and I won't forget. Besides . . .' She smiled at her companion affectionately. 'I'll *want* to get in touch with you, for I'll have so much to tell you.'

'There's a good girl. I'll be waiting. Oh dear—I think we'd better go and collect our things, for as soon as we dock, the immigration officials will come on board. They won't keep us long. James is meeting me—I imagine you will be met?'

Kate nodded, and felt the excitement sweep over her again. She looked at the shore and told herself that the threatened disasters might never happen. Both Mrs. Kelly and Mrs. McCormack were at the age when they got flustered easily and imagined the worst. Mr. Lister would see that everything went smoothly—for the sake of his daughter. 'Yes— I'm being met at the docks,' Kate said.

Together they went down to their cabin to collect their personal luggage and see that everything else was ready to be taken ashore. As they moved round the small cabin, making sure they had left nothing behind, Mrs. McCormack apologised. 'My dear, I am sorry I had to inflict Mrs. Kelly on you—' Her voice dropped to a conspiratorial whisper. 'She is dying with curiosity to know all about you, so I thought it best for her to know the truth. She's the biggest scandalmonger out here, and if

13

she's going to talk—and she can't help it—I wanted her to have the accurate facts, poor dear.'

'But why should she talk about me?' Kate asked, dismayed.

Mrs. McCormack did not answer her for a moment. She was rummaging through her expensive crocodile leather handbag frantically. 'This is a small community of English folk, my dear, and there's always talk. Especially when a pretty young girl like you comes out to take up the unusual—for this country—post of nursery governess.'

'Why do you always call her *poor dear?* I hate people who gossip!'

Mrs. McCormack stopped rummaging in her handbag for a moment, and smiled tolerantly. 'My dear, I pity her because she has so empty a life that she has nothing else to do but talk.' She looked into the bag again and gave a triumphant cry. 'Ah!' She produced her passport. 'For an awful moment, I thought I had lost it.' She looked at Kate's face and chuckled. 'You must think I'm a silly old fusspot.'

'I think you're a darling,' Kate said. 'Please—you've never let me thank you properly for all you did for me. Having you has made all the difference to my journey. When I was so ill—'

Mrs. McCormack's face turned turkey-cock red. Gratitude embarrassed her so.

14

'I've loved every moment of it. My dear, we'd better hurry. Ah . . .' she said as the ship gave a light jolt. 'That mean's we've docked. Come on!'

They went up to the lounge, to wait their turn. The passengers only passing through Lourenço Marques had already gone ashore to see the town, but there were still quite a number of people, all talking and laughing, saying last-minute farewells, exchanging names and addresses. Apart from Mrs. McCormack, Kate realised that there was no one on board she would want to see again. The ship-board romances she had often read of in novels were not, apparently, for her. There had been some young men on board, but oh—how very young they had seemed when compared with Randel Lister!

Finally the time of waiting was over and Kate's papers were stamped. She went out on deck. Mrs. McCormack was already there, leaning over the rail, gazing eagerly at a group of people standing round the gangway. Suddenly she gave an excited shriek, and Kate saw a tall, fair-haired man waving up at the ship.

'There's James. James, my son,' Mrs. McCormack said proudly. 'Can you see your Mr. Lister?'

Kate gazed hard, but could see no one remotely resembling the tall, dark-haired man whose arrival she awaited with such breathless excitement.

'No—' she said, rather sadly.

'Probably caught up in a conference. He'll be along in a moment. I'll just go down and meet James.' Mrs. McCormack went into the lounge, on her way down to the decks below and the gangway.

Kate leant against the rail, answering those people who spoke to her but watching the people on the dock. She felt remote, detached from reality, conscious only of her impatience to start her new life.

As she stood there, small dark cold fears crept into her mind. Mr. Lister's eyes could be very cold. He would demand perfection from his employees. Suppose Rose did not like her new governess? Kate told herself that most children liked her. As for Mrs. Kelly's dour prophecies—why let them worry her? After all, Kate knew very well that she was good at adapting herself to fresh and even strange situations, and why shouldn't she learn how to live in a Portuguese household for six months?

'Kate!' Mrs. McCormack's voice made Kate turn round. Hurrying along the deck, a little breathless, came Mrs. McCormack, smiling up at the tall, pleasant-looking man by her side. 'This is my son—James. And James, this is Kate Williams.'

Kate stared up at the tall man and liked his very blue eyes and thought what a nice smile he had. His mother had certainly not exaggerated about his charm. Now he held Kate's hand for a second and his eyes began to twinkle.

'Mother has casually mentioned your name.' His laughter made Kate chuckle and then they were laughing in the shared amusement. James's mother beamed at them.

'I knew you'd like one another,' she said happily.

James smiled at Kate. 'Mr. Lister may have been delayed. Could I give you a lift?'

Kate hesitated, not liking to admit that she did not know Mr. Lister's home address—not even his business one. Suddenly that seemed rather witless of her and she shivered a little. Supposing Mr. Lister had changed his mind? Or was ill and did not turn up? As she looked into James's frankly friendly face, her fear vanished. She had the McCormacks. She need only telephone them. That gave her a feeling of security. 'I think I should wait,' she told them thoughtfully.

James nodded. 'Maybe so. You know, I heard a rumour about you, but I didn't believe it.'

'A rumour—of what?' Kate asked, rejoicing in the hot sun on her back and these two nice people standing by her side, making what was something of an ordeal so much easier to bear. Now if only Mr. Lister would turn up!

James was smiling. 'Everyone heard that Randel Lister was importing an English governess for his daughter, but no one believed it.'

'Why ever not?' A chill ran down Kate's back. 'Why didn't you believe it?' She frowned. 'Do you know Mr. Lister well?'

James shrugged. 'We belong to the same club. I played golf with him once. We speak when we meet. That sort of acquaintance, you know.'

'But why didn't you believe the rumour?' James's mother asked, practically taking the words out of Kate's mouth.

He looked uncomfortable, as if regretting his casual words now.

'Please tell me,' Kate begged.

He tried to make light of it, but still looked ill at ease. 'You know what rumours are. We're always hearing things. Actually we didn't think the Dominguez would agree.'

'The Dominguez?' Kate and Mrs. McCormack spoke at once.

'Senhora Dominguez is the child's grandmother—but it was Mariana, really—'

'Mariana?' Kate echoed, feeling more bewildered than ever.

James's face showed the struggle inside him. 'It's probably all talk, but—well, to cut it short, Mariana is Lister's sister-in-law. She is extremely beautiful, very selfish, and most possessive.' James's voice was crisp. 'It's obvious that she intends to marry Lister, but how he feels about it is—well, anyone's guess.'

18

James shrugged. 'Most men think he's mad to hesitate. Mariana is a very beautiful and passionate creature.'

'She sounds most unpleasant,' Mrs. McCormack said firmly, looking at her son with the nearest approach to a frown Kate could imagine on her face. 'James—I cannot understand, if you know so much about her, how it is that I've never met her.'

James gave her that affectionate smile that Kate was already beginning to look for, as he said, 'Mama darling, she isn't the type of woman you would introduce to your mother.'

The answer seemed to satisfy Mrs. McCormack, but James's eyes were twinkling as he looked at Kate. Kate's drooping spirits lifted. How could she feel gloomy when she had friends like these?

'But if she is that type,' Mrs. McCormack went on thoughtfully, 'surely Mr. Lister . . .'

James looked at his watch. 'I told you she was selfish, and I think Lister knows that. His engaging Kate to look after his child must have been rather a snub for Mariana. I can imagine how angry she must be.'

Kate took a deep breath and tried to ignore the desolation that was creeping back. It looked as though she had a tough job ahead of her.

'Do you know Mr. Lister's daughter?' she asked.

'Rose? Yes, she's a nice little kid, but so old-fashioned. Very Portuguese and sweet, but not in the least like an English child. She is very sedate, very pale and well-behaved. Frankly, a darned sight too well behaved, if you ask me. I'm not surprised Lister thinks it's time to make a change. A pity he didn't think of it before. The child needs a lot of loving, and to be taught to laugh and enjoy life.'

'But her grandmother must love her. After all, she has looked after her for all these years,' Kate put in hastily.

James looked amused. 'I don't think people like the Dominguez know what we mean by love. Rose is accepted so long as she does not make a nuisance of herself, but I imagine that if she behaved like a normal healthy child, she would soon get punished.' He looked at his watch again. 'I really am sorry, Mother, but we must go. Don't worry, Kate.' He turned to the quiet slim girl and took her hand gently, looking into her somewhat forlorn face with a reassuring smile. 'You mustn't let us worry you. I'm sure everything will work out all right. Lister is no fool. He will have made the position clear to the Dominguez. We'll be seeing you soon.'

'Of course,' Mrs. McCormack said quickly. 'Kate has promised to telephone me the instant she is settled in. Then she will come round and see us a lot. I'm looking forward to having her companionship.' She smiled at Kate. 'You have promised, dear child.'

20

Kate smiled. 'Of course I have. It's just wonderful for me to have you here—makes all the difference in the world,' she added warmly.

To Kate's surprise—for Mrs. McCormack was not a demonstrative woman—Kate felt herself warmly kissed. James shook her by the hand, giving her that nice smile of his, and then she was alone, watching James help his mother down the steep gangway. At the foot both turned, waved, and then vanished behind the trucks as the great derricks began to swing into action and everyone started shouting. Kate felt horribly alone. She looked round wildly. If only she knew where Mr. Lister lived. It was dreadful waiting—wondering—fearing.

James had said everything would be all right? But had that just been to comfort her? What of the Dominguez family? Would they talk English? Resent her—refuse to let her try to make them like her?

She made herself watch the huge cranes move majestically, and even spared an admiring thought for the clever men who sat perched high in their little cabins, and worked these huge machines so accurately. She drifted to the other side of the ship. How beautiful everything was. Wasn't she lucky?

Lucky, too, because Mr. Stowe had persuaded Mr. Lister to let her travel out by sea rather than by air, because he said she should have a few weeks' holiday between the two jobs. The voyage had been wonderful, but, better still, it had introduced her to the McCormacks. How much more worried she would have been feeling but for them.

Kate remembered the days when she had been looking after the Stanfords' children—both darlings, like their parents. And how miserable she had been when they announced they were going to America. And how thrilled when they asked her to go with them. Then had ensued a few hectic weeks preparing for the journey, and—Kate shivered and instinctively closed her eyes—then her father had been killed in a car crash. Naturally Kate had stayed at home with her mother, for they needed one another badly. Both were bitterly unhappy. In addition, Kate's mother was a semi-invalid, though Kate's friends always said that to hear her mother's plans and see her happy, eager face, they found it hard to realise that she practically spent her life in a wheelchair.

Kate had told Randel Lister this at her first interview. Now, remembering, she saw the thoughtful look on his face. He said nothing. It was only when she got home that night that she found he had been to see her mother.

'What a fine man,' her mother had said. 'How devoted he was to his wife. I wonder he has not married again, though, if only for the child's sake. You must take the job, Kate darling. It's a chance in a million. And only for six months. I promise you I'll be all right.'

Kate had hesitated, yet had known that she would hurt her mother far more by not going than by leaving her. Her mother could not bear it if she was made to feel a burden. Active, she had strong arms, and easily swung herself in and out of her chair, for she loathed being helped. They had good neighbours on either side of their house. Kate frankly admitted she longed to go. It would be fun to look after a child again, and how romantic Lourenço Marques sounded.

Now, staring blindly at the sea, Kate wondered how it was that in all those hours of discussing the job neither she nor her mother had thought that there might be any unpleasantness or difficulties. Why had they never thought of it from the grandmother's angle? Even so—James had said it was mainly Mariana who would cause trouble.

Mariana—beautiful, selfish, passionate—

Suddenly Kate realised she was on the wrong side of the ship. She hurried back to the dockside, but the ship was almost deserted and there was no sign of a tall, good-looking dark man. At that moment, a tall boy came up to her.

'Why, Ned!' Kate greeted him, and smiled. Very shy, very young, even now he spoke nervously, although they had often danced and chatted together.

'I say, are you still here?' He went bright red and stumbled on: 'That's a silly thing to say, for I can see you are. What I mean is . . .'

Kate nodded. She tried to sound cheerful. 'I hope I haven't been forgotten.' She glanced at her watch and was shocked to see how long she had been waiting. Something must have gone wrong.

Ned's laugh was like his voice and not always under control. Now he giggled rather shrilly and then looked embarrassed. 'I say, what fun if you have been forgotten. You can come on to Mombasa with us. Have you practised your Portuguese?'

'Not much, I'm afraid,' Kate confessed. Ned, who knew some Portuguese, had been trying to teach her with the aid of a phrase book.

'Let's have a bash,' he suggested. *'Bom dias.'*

'Bom dias.' Kate gravely returned the greeting, which meant 'good morning.'

He frowned. 'Not quite right. Try it again.'

Time flew, and Kate was struggling to say *Muito obrigado, senhor* while both laughed, when a shadow fell on them. Kate turned. Mr. Lister was watching them, frowning.

He spoke almost harshly. 'I should have thought you had enough sense to go ashore when I failed to turn up. I was delayed and must now waste more time getting you through the Customs. Surely you could have managed that on your own?'

Kate's face stung. It was as if he had slapped her. She felt rather than saw poor Ned quietly

24

fading out of the scene, and caught a glimpse of his distressed young face. Then the injustice of Mr. Lister's remark gave her courage.

'You told me to wait on the ship. In any case, you forgot to give me your address.'

Randel Lister stared at the slim, valiant girl facing him and she saw the anger drain out of his face as embarrassment replaced it.

'You're quite right. I expressly told you to wait on board. And I forgot to give you my address. How could I have been so stupid?' He spoke thoughtfully. 'I must apologise.' Abruptly he smiled. It was just as if someone had waved a magic wand, for a totally different man stood there. 'Apologise,' he continued, 'not only for my forgetfulness but also for losing my temper. Not a nice welcome, I'm afraid.' And—again—he gave that wonderful smile.

It was a totally different sort of smile from James's. Where James's smile was sweet and friendly—Mr. Lister's was thrilling.

'You must have been growing a little alarmed,' Mr. Lister went on.

Kate tried to smile. 'I was—a little.'

'I'm sure you were. I've had a hot, frustrating morning, but that's no excuse for the way I snapped at you. Am I forgiven?'

Kate was smiling now. 'Of course you are, Mr. Lister. But I wondered what I ought to do. I was afraid if I went ashore we might miss one another and—'

25

'You were quite right,' he said, but now his voice was curt, indicating that the matter needed no further discussion. 'What is your cabin number? I have a boy to get your luggage. No doubt you have some farewells to make, but get them over quickly and meet me at the gangway.'

Kate hurried to find Ned and to assure him everything was all right.

'I don't like him—nor the way he spoke to you,' Ned said stubbornly.

Kate could laugh now. 'Neither did I. I was quite scared. But he did apologise, Ned, and that's more than many people will do, isn't it?'

She hurried to the gangway, but, despite her haste, Mr. Lister was waiting impatiently. Kate could see the African boy who was holding her cases.

They hurried ashore, Mr. Lister's long strides making Kate almost run to keep up with him. The customs officials did not look very friendly and eyed Kate with suspicion. She felt safe with Mr. Lister being so impressive as he towered above them. All the same, they all spoke very fast, waving their hands about, rolling their eyes skywards, almost tearing out their hair. Kate began to wonder if she had unconsciously committed some crime. Mr. Lister's voice changed, became impatient. Then everyone was miraculously laughing, the shouting ceased, and the officials chalked crosses on her unopened cases and ushered them out of the building.

Somehow Kate had not been prepared for the shock of the sunshine in the street. It was a violent heat as the waves reflected back from the road and pavement and the sun shone down. Her blue linen suit was suddenly much too heavy. She wished she had dark glasses and a shady hat. She followed Mr. Lister to a big red car, the kind she had only seen before in films. A uniformed African driver slid out from behind the steering wheel and came to open the car door, and then to pack her luggage in the boot.

Kate got into the car. To her utter amazement, Mr. Lister closed the door and spoke to her through the window, curtly. 'I haven't the time to take you up, but you're expected. I'll be along this afternoon to see how you have settled in.' His voice changed, then—almost as if the distress Kate was sure her face was betraying, forced him to say more—'Unfortunately, I have a very important interview for which I'm already late.' He turned and spoke to the driver, and the car moved away.

Kate felt like crying—for one awful moment. So had she an important interview—meeting his daughter for the first time. Or didn't Mr. Lister think that 'important'? She was already dreading the meeting with the Dominguez as well—and to have to meet them

27

alone made it a thousand times worse.

She took a deep breath and looked round, trying to show interest in the unusual scene. First there was a rather drab, slummy area by the docks, but then the car moved out into a wide street between skyscrapers, big shops, with everywhere these great shining cars. It seemed to Kate that they crawled, for there was so much traffic and traffic lights every few yards. Ahead of her she saw an enormous church with a great cross—and then there was a pavement café with people sitting at tables under striped umbrellas, sipping drinks.

As the lights turned red, the car braked and stopped. And a voice cried urgently, 'Kate!'

Startled, Kate turned, and saw Mr. Lister running towards the car. He looked hot—red as a lobster—and could hardly speak for breathlessness. His words surprised her still more. 'Are you sure you'll be all right?'

Kate's young, generous heart forgave him instantly. How wonderful of him to run after her. How well he must know the short cuts through the streets.

'Of course I will,' she told him reassuringly. 'A new job is always rather an ordeal, but . . .'

He nodded, his breathing easier now, but his eyes still concerned. 'I know. I wish I could come with you, but . . .' Somewhere a clock chimed and he looked horrified. 'Is it so late? You will be all right, Kate?' he repeated, his voice reassuring, yet to Kate it sounded as though he wanted to reassure himself as well as her. 'It's just that you looked so young and lost—just like a forlorn waif.'

Kate's cheeks were hot. Why must everyone harp on her youth? Nineteen wasn't so young.

'Don't forget I'm used to working—and to meeting people,' she said a little stiffly.

'I know, but . . .'

There was still indecision in his mind. He was obviously weighing up the importance of his interview as against the importance of escorting her. Somehow she was not surprised —though rather disappointed—when his interview won. Mr. Lister was the kind of man for whom personal considerations would always take second place.

All round them, cars were beginning to hoot, and a big white bus lumbered by, the driver leaning out of the window to shout something obviously rude as he passed. Mr. Lister's chauffeur looked anxiously over his shoulder, and Randel nodded. 'I'll see you later,' he said curtly to Kate, and stepped back.

Kate turned her head and watched him for as long as she could see him. Rather to her surprise, she saw that he, too, was watching the car until it was out of sight. She felt happier for the little incident. It showed he understood some of her difficulties. That he was human.

Feeling better, she looked round with interest. They passed a park full of gracefully waving palm trees, with flower beds full of colour. The car swung round a corner and there was a big hotel, the front of the building curved like the prow of a ship. On they went past white villas with brightly painted front doors and roofs, and window boxes full of flowers. Kate looked at them eagerly and wondered what sort of home Mr. Lister could have. It would be sure to be very bright and modern, probably with contemporary furniture and lots of colour.

Suddenly the car swung off the main road and went down a steep side street. Ahead of her she could see glimpses of the bright sun showing through the trees. The car stopped outside a square grey stone building.

Startled, Kate stared up at it, for printed on the stone in faded white letters were the words PENSAO FADORA.

She stared, amazed, as the chauffeur opened the car door for her and then went to the boot to get her cases. She looked up in horror at the dingy building. Mr. Lister could not live here!

But the chauffeur went into the house with the luggage, opening the swing doors with his shoulder, then came back to her, waited while she got out of the car, touched his cap, got into it, and drove away before she could speak.

What could she have said? She stood very still, staring up at the house. There must be some mistake. Mr. Lister was a wealthy man.

He would not live in an obviously third-rate pension like this, surely? He was a man of character and strong personality. She could not see him living in such surroundings. But what was she to do? It must be the place. The luggage was inside.

Slowly she pushed open the swing doors and went into the dark, cool hall. There was a curved reception counter with an open ledger on it. A few wicker chairs were grouped round a wide staircase. There was an archway, covered by a curtain of wooden beads. Everything was clean and highly polished, but it looked so drab, and had a musty smell.

Mr. Lister could not live here. There must be some mistake.

Then she thought of something else. Perhaps she was to live here—and go to her job daily? But surely not. Mr. Lister had stressed so firmly that he wanted his little daughter to spend her whole day with her English nursery-governess—and that surely meant living in?

When she saw the telephone, she moved towards it impulsively, going to her handbag for the note she had made of Mrs. McCormack's telephone number. Then Kate sighed, closing her handbag again. How could she telephone and say she did not like the look of the place, and was—let's be honest, she told herself—rather frightened?

She drew a deep breath. This must be the

right place—it was just that it was so disappointing.

A sound made her look up, to see a young man leaping down the stairs, halting abruptly when he saw her, his hand on the iron banister. He was slender, dressed in a white suit, his skin was olive, his raven hair smooth, his dark eyes bright with curiosity.

'I can be of some aid, senhora?' he enquired politely.

Kate stared at him. For whom should she ask? Mr. Lister had given her no name. True, James had spoken of the Senhora Dom . . . Domin . . . If only she had written the name down. But then, of course, she had never expected to be in such an awkward position. She had been sure Mr. Lister would introduce her personally to the family.

She wondered miserably if she looked as foolish as she felt, standing there as if struck dumb. The young man came down the stairs rapidly and stood too close to her. She did not like the look in his eyes and found herself moving away a little.

'My name—I am Antonio Vidal, at your service, senhora,' he said, with a bow. He smiled at Kate, took her hand and kissed it.

Without thinking, she snatched her hand away, and then felt more foolish than ever, for he looked amused. It was probably a Portuguese custom and she had acted like a naïve schoolgirl.

'The senhora—' the young man said softly, and leaned closer towards her.

Kate backed away, frightened and wondering how to cope with the situation, and remembering all Mrs. McCormack's warnings about amorous young Portuguese. To her great relief, the bead curtains rattled, parted, and a girl came through the archway.

Kate turned to look at her, thankful that the interruption had rescued her from what might have been an embarrassing moment. She saw a young girl of her own age, but one who looked so unhappy that it shocked her. A girl with eyes deep-set in her sallow cheeks, with a sulky mouth. She moved very awkwardly, with jerky uncoordinated movements as she leant on a stick and touched the wall or chairs as she passed them.

'*Bom dias,*' the girl began, and switched to English. 'Can I, perhaps, be of some assistance?' She had an unusual voice, Kate thought. It was low, and sounded desperate, almost pleading.

The young man moved away. '*Adeus, Menina,*' he said haughtily, and went out through the swing doors.

The girl's face puckered. For a moment Kate thought that she was going to cry, but, as she watched, the girl bit her lower lip hard and went on moving, with her jerky, clumsy movements, behind the counter.

Kate wondered how to explain who she was.

33

'Mr. Lister's chauffeur brought me here,' she began slowly.

The girl looked up and smiled. Kate was amazed. Why, she looked quite pretty. And her eyes offered friendship. Was there also compassion in them?

'Ah—you are the Engleesh mees? For the little Rosa, no?'

Kate sighed. She was not sure whether to be glad or sorry, but at least she was expected. But here, of all places! She could not understand it.

'I understand I am expected,' she said stiffly.

'But of course—' The girl clapped her hands. A young African boy, wearing white shorts and jacket, came running. He listened to her quiet words, grabbed Kate's cases, and shot up the staircase as if pursued by bandits.

The eyes of the two girls met, and they smiled.

'Do not be persuaded by his manner,' the Portuguese girl told Kate. 'He is a lazy rascal, but when he thinks our eyes are opened, and there is hope for a . . . a . . . I do not know your word for it, but you will understand. Not that it is necessary—of a certainty not.' She smiled at Kate. 'To them, a little means so much. You will follow him, pliz, mees?'

'Yes, of course. Thank you.' Kate hesitated. Looking at the girl, she longed to ask questions. Yet wouldn't that be rather undignified? And disloyal to Mr. Lister? She straightened her shoulders and faced the stairs. This ordeal had to be faced some time and she could no longer postpone it. She turned and smiled at the girl, who stood by the counter and watched her with a strange look in her unhappy eyes, and then Kate went upstairs.

She saw that the carpet was a good one, the walls were clean, everything polished brightly. Yet there was a deadness about the building, a sort of hush—an uncomfortable, frightening hush as though people were hiding and watching and listening.

'Don't be so silly,' she told herself crossly. She was letting her imagination run away with her thoughts. Yet the thought persisted again and again—how could a man like Mr. Lister bear to live in a place like this? It did not make sense.

On the different landings she caught glimpses of straight corridors and darkly curtained windows. She saw no one. At the end of the third flight of stairs there was a closed door.

Even as she approached it, it flew open and the African boy dashed out, pausing to look expectantly at her. She was sorry she had no Portuguese money, so half smiled, spreading out her hands hopelessly. The boy gave her a dejected look, ducked his head, and went by her, leaving the door ajar.

CHAPTER II

Kate hesitated before the half-open door, for she could hear someone's excited voice, though of course she could not understand a word of it. She knocked rather timidly. No answer. She waited again and then knocked a little louder. She felt silly standing there, and wondered if whoever was talking might imagine she was eavesdropping.

'*Un momento!*' the angry voice cried out.

Kate waited nervously. How horribly gloomy it all was. She stared down a long passage. There was a window at the far end, but dark curtains were drawn across it. At last the voice stopped and she could hear what sounded like a telephone receiver being slammed down.

A door in the passage was jerked open and a tall woman came out of a room. She was dressed in black, the long strings of jet beads round her neck swinging as she walked, and her olive skin was beaded with perspiration. A heavily built woman, her snow-white hair was piled high on her head, and she was patting it as she came down the passage. She wore no make-up and her lips were an odd sort of blue colour as she peered at Kate through half-shut eyes.

Kate listened to the Portuguese words and

smiled apologetically.

'Mr. Lister . . .' she began.

The elderly woman stopped speaking and her mouth formed a peculiar smile. 'Ah—the Englese miss. Enter, if you will.'

Kate obeyed, thinking with relief that at least someone talked English. She followed the Portuguese woman into the room she had just left and sank obediently into a chair when told. Then she stared round her, and it was like a nightmare; there must be some mistake, she thought wildly. A man like Randel Lister could not live here!

'Mees Williams? I am the Senhora Amelita Dominguez, the grandmother of Rosa,' the elderly woman said grandly.

Kate bowed. 'How do you do,' she murmured, and thought for the thousandth time what an idiotic greeting it sounded. 'Rose—I am looking forward to meeting her.' Kate was ashamed of her voice, for it shook slightly. She wished she was not so nervous. Maybe it was because she had been so excited and now everything had fallen flat—maybe just the atmosphere in the room as the Senhora Dominguez went on peering at her, giving funny little rabbit-like nibbles at her lower lip as she did so.

'Ah—Rosa is walking herself with the housemaid. Doubtless she will be back here *un momento.* The Senhor Lister—he did not come with you.'

37

It was a statement, not a question. The harsh voice was uneven as if the speaker was suppressing some strong emotion. Kate wondered if it was anger or resentment. Had the Senhora been talking to Mr. Lister on the telephone?

'He has an appointment. Doubtless he will be with us later,' Kate said, and then stopped, appalled. She looked nervously at the Senhora, afraid lest it be thought she had been mimicking the older woman. Odd how infectious a pedantic way of speech can be.

There was silence. Kate tried not to fidget. She was very hungry indeed, for breakfast had been hours before and she had eaten very little. The clock on the table said nearly midday. It was a dark unfriendly room with heavy furniture, and to Kate, in her tired over-emotional state, there was something menacing about it.

They both heard the child's voice at the same time. Both turned to look at the door. Kate's spirits rose a little—this was what she had been waiting for.

'Rosa!' the Senhora called, and added some words in Portuguese.

The door that had been half closed was pushed open and a child stood there. Kate's heart seemed to jerk with the shock. She understood now what Mr. Lister had meant when he told her, 'Rose reminds me of a plant kept too long in a dark cupboard.'

It was an exact description. The child was tall—too tall and thin for her age. She wore a starched white frock of broderie anglaise—an old-fashioned frock, too long, with a full skirt and, obviously, several starched petticoats beneath it. She stood there very quietly with her hands clasped and stared at Kate.

Her eyes were huge and dark and there was something pathetically old about her little thin face with its pale skin. Her soft flaxen hair had been scraped back from her high forehead, and up at the back of her neck, as well—strained across her scalp and twisted into a tight chignon on top of her head. Not even one little soft wisp of hair was free.

Kate stared back, shivering a little. Her vivid imagination pictured how strong and ruthless must be the hands that brushed that soft hair every day, twisting, imprisoning it. It was lovely hair and should have been like a cloud of spun silk on the child's back, capturing the sunshine, bouncing lightly as she walked.

Kate went on staring—mentally changing the stiff uncomfortable dress for a gay cotton frock, short white socks and sandals instead of the long black stockings and heavy shoes.

These things Kate knew she could alter—but could she ever hope to wipe out that look of utter desolation, of hopeless fear, that shone from the child's eyes? No child should look like that. How could her father have left it so late before seeing how badly she needed help? Was it too late already?

Kate's mouth was suddenly dry as she tried to think of the best way to make the first move. Whatever happened, it must not be a false one.

She held out her hand. 'Hullo, Rose—I'm Kate.'

Then the most awful thing happened. The child's face began to quiver and she turned and ran from the room, screaming, 'Anna! Anna . . . Anna . . . !'

Kate's hand dropped to her side. She looked at the Senhora and saw the triumph flash in those beady eyes before the Senhora lowered her eyelids. The harsh voice held a false sympathy that was pure condescension. 'You must have the patience. What would you—she is so young, and you are a foreign stranger.' Her words were dipped in acid. 'I do not think it will be easy for you,' the Senhora finished smugly.

'I do not expect it to be,' Kate said stiffly, feeling anger throb through her. So they *were* going to be difficult? She recognised the threat behind the words, and all that was young and gallant in her rose to the surface. For a moment she felt strong enough to do battle with a thousand dragons; somehow that child must be rescued, helped. Then her temporary confidence vanished as she faced facts. The first thing was to know what had been said to make the child so terrified of her.

Kate stood up. It would not be easy, but she must try. Most important of all, she must walk warily. Whatever happened, the Dominguez must be given no chance to complain of her behaviour, nor be able to accuse her of rudeness.

'Senhora,' she said with great politeness, 'is it permitted for me to see my room? I should like to wash and unpack.'

She found herself forming odd stiff sentences, her very anger and fear making her mind slow. As she watched the older woman, Kate saw the beady eyes were bright with amused triumph, and knew that Round One had been won by the Dominguez.

'But of course, mees . . .'

The Senhora told Kate how to find her room. It was the door on the right at the end of the corridor. Then she turned away, picked up a piece of material and bent over it, and began to stitch.

Kate flushed. Dismissal—and indifference. All right, she could take it. But her cheeks were still burning as she went down the passage and found her room, where the suitcases were waiting.

She stood in the doorway and was filled with dismay.

The room was dark and dingy, such a striking contrast to the sunshine and blue sea and white villas of the town. Dark green curtains were drawn to shut out the sunlight.

41

The high narrow bed had a mattress that proved, on testing, to be very hard. There was a dressing-table with a spotted mirror that hideously distorted her face as she stared into it. In the corner was a small washbasin, but the water only trickled slowly out of the cold tap and none at all from the hot one.

Trying to fight her depression, Kate jerked back the curtains, and for the first time felt happier. The curtains had covered french windows and there was a small balcony.

As she stepped outside, the hot air greeted her. She stared over the rooftops of the many little houses, right over the tops of the palm trees which moved very slowly in the slight breeze—and there was the sea.

It was so wonderfully blue. Even as she watched, a small cloud passed over the sun, and miraculously the sea changed to a dark aquamarine colour. There was barely a ripple on that great expanse of blue water—water that stretched miles and miles away—the Indian Ocean.

The balcony was small, but there was a chair to sit on. Kate sat down and drew a long deep breath gathering fresh courage, telling herself that this would be her haven when things became almost unbearable. For they would— she knew that now.

After a short rest, drinking in the absolute beauty and peace of the scene before her, Kate went back into the little room and looked at it with new eyes. Maybe it would not be so bad when she had put out her photographs. A few flowers—and perhaps some cheap gay material for a bedspread, and even curtains, if that would not offend the Dominguez. Oh dear, she would indeed have to tread carefully. But she felt suddenly that it could be done, and as she thought of Rose's white, peaked, frightened face, she was determined to do it.

She unpacked, fighting the lethargy that the intense heat filled her with, hanging the grey Terylene skirt in the wardrobe, realising that most of her clothes would be far too warm. Luckily she had a flowered nylon frock and two cotton ones, and then, as she put away her good blue cocktail suit of watered satin, she was wondering if she would have any use for that.

Mr. Lister had told her not to buy new clothes.

'You will need a special wardrobe for Mozambique,' he had said. 'They would be useless for England when you return, so I shall expect to pay for your clothes out there and you must look on them as a uniform. The temperature reaches over a hundred and ten degrees, so you will understand that you need very light tropical materials.'

Kate's mother had said the offer was generous, but Kate could understand now. Already she had seen that she would need to change her frocks and undies several times a day because of the humidity.

Now she changed into the lightest frock she owned—a finely checked chiffon frock of palest yellow. Ten minutes later, she might never have washed or changed, for she felt just as hot as ever as she sat waiting with the door ajar, in the hope of encouraging a draught.

But sitting still had never pleased Kate, and already her desire to see Rose again brought her to her feet, making her brush her hair with long swinging strokes as she forced herself to be patient. As she did so, she had her first chance. She heard a footstep. Hardly daring to breathe, she put down the hairbrush and picked up a Portuguese dictionary, sitting on the edge of the bed and deliberately keeping her eyes away from the doorway. She had thought of her first approach. Let a child *help* you—that was the advice she had been given once.

'Lavor as maos . . . Bom dias . . .' she said laboriously, and her tongue stumbled as she tried to say, *'Obriobrigado . . .'*

Her heart seemed to stop for a second as she heard soft laughter, and a young voice correct her. 'But no—no! It is *Lavor as maos— bom dias.'*

The words sounded enchanting in that young voice. Still keeping her eyes on the dictionary, Kate tried again. Once more she tried and stumbled over the words and waited. But this time there was silence.

44

She took a long deep breath and decided that she must risk something.

'Oh dear,' she said sadly. 'I never will learn to speak Portuguese and I simply *must!*'

The door closed softly. She heard tiptoeing footsteps on the polished floor. Still fighting the temptation to turn her head, Kate discovered she could see Rose in the mirror. The child was standing by her side, her face timid, her whole body poised, as if for flight. And the child spoke again.

'Why must you learn to speak Portuguese?'

Kate gently crossed her fingers. She kept her voice very soft and low.

'Because I want to talk to Rosa.'

As she waited breathlessly, she wondered if she had done right. While unpacking, she had thought a lot about the right approach towards the little girl, and had decided that no matter what her father said, the child must not be rushed. Logically, therefore, Rose must still be called Rosa, as that was the name the child had always been called. Whatever they did, they must not separate her forcibly from her familiar life. Rather, she must be weaned. But would Mr. Lister understand that? Kate wondered anxiously.

Now Kate could feel the child's soft breath on her cheek—that meant she must be near. Yet Kate felt the moment to look at Rosa had not yet come, for one false move could undo everything.

45

'But I speak English,' Rosa said slowly.

Now Kate dared to turn and look at her, and saw the earnestness on the small pale face and met the dark unflinching eyes.

'Yet,' Kate said, 'when I spoke to you in English, you were afraid.'

Rosa shook her head. 'I wasn't afraid because of that.'

Kate's mouth was dry with nervousness. Trickles of water slid down her spine. Please God, she found herself praying, please God, guide me.

'Then why were you afraid?' Kate asked gently.

She watched the tip of Rosa's tongue run nervously over her lips—saw the indecision in the dark eyes, the effort the child was making as she began, 'Because . . .'

And then there was an interruption. Kate could have cried with dismay.

'Rosa—Rosa . . .' called an angry, impatient voice.

The child changed instantly. Her face grew old and the eyes dark with fear, and without a word or another glance she turned silently and opened the door very quietly, vanishing as she pulled it to behind her.

The very stealth of her movements shocked Kate more than she could have said. At that age, to be so afraid—so used to creeping out of rooms!

Yet she had gained something—the child

had shown confidence in her. Still, it was hard not to feel black misery because she had been so near and then . . . Don't be silly, she told herself crossly, you can't win confidences with a few words. At least Rosa came to you . . . And had been going to say what she was afraid of.

Feeling slightly happier, Kate welcomed the sound of a gong. Lunch!

She hurried down the corridor. The Senhora Amelita Dominguez was waiting for her, her large flabby hands folded patiently as if Kate had been keeping her sitting there for hours on end, her black bright eyes hidden by those heavy hooded lids. When she saw Kate she rose and solemnly led the way to the dining-room. There was an oval walnut table laid with shining silver and glass, and curtains over the window which only allowed a brown twilight to fill the room.

Kate saw that only two places were laid as she sat down in the chair indicated. Her heart sank. So Rosa would not eat with them. The Senhora rang a silver bell and a very plump African girl in a bright red frock and stiffly starched white apron brought in a heavily laden tray which she laid on the sideboard. The Senhora rose majestically and went to it.

'*Un momento,*' she said, and Kate waited silently, watching the Senhora serve meat and vegetables on two separate plates which the girl carried away on the tray.

Then Kate was served and she ate hungrily, enjoying the perfectly cooked food, despite its spiciness and highly seasoned taste. She wondered why she was being honoured by the Senhora's company, for she had quite expected to eat alone with Rosa. She did hope it was not going to be a permanent habit, though, for the oppressive silence made eating difficult. She glanced at the Senhora, who was eating rapidly as if she was starved, her face absorbed.

'The child does not eat with us, Senhora Dominguez?' Kate said politely.

The older woman did not stop eating, but spoke through her mouth full of food. 'The *bébé* always eats with Anna, for it is better so.'

Who was Anna? Kate hesitated, looking at the Senhora's forbidding face, realising that to the older woman the meal was a solemn function and not to be spoiled by idle chatter. After that Kate ate silently, enjoying the rich, creamy sweet and welcoming the small cup of strong black coffee.

It was odd, then, the effect that the meal seemed to have had on the Senhora, for quite suddenly she relaxed, her fat hands cupping the tiny cup as she rested her elbows on the table, gazing vacantly above Kate's head and talking in English. She sounded as if she was thinking aloud, yet Kate realised that if that was so, she would surely have spoken in Portuguese.

'This is a thing I do not understand . . .' The

harsh voice was almost dreamy, the stern face relaxed for a moment. 'Something I will never understand. When one is so beautiful . . . So desirable, so . . . Ah . . . !' She nodded her head solemnly and the heavy jet beads jangled noisily. She clutched them with one hand and went on talking. 'Life—how droll it is. That one so lovely . . .'

None of it made sense to Kate. Yet she had the uncomfortable feeling of being talked at.

'She loves him with her whole heart. How can one be so cruel?' The voice droned on.

Kate stirred uncomfortably. How hot it was—not a window open. Was the Senhora talking about Mr. Lister's first wife, perhaps? Yet she used the present tense.

'It is not wise to break a person's heart . . . Not wise nor safe,' the Senhora continued, but now she lifted her head and her eyelids, and stared at Kate. Black, bright, beady eyes, filled with hate. Abruptly the Senhora's voice changed, came alive, vicious. 'I do not think the Englese mees will find Mozambique a healthy country.'

Kate almost jumped out of her chair with the shock of the changed voice, the animosity on that face. Now they stared at one another silently. Kate wondered what to say. Was it a threat? A warning? The Senhora was talking about Mariana—the beautiful, passionate, possessive, selfish Mariana.

It was a relief that the door opened at that

moment and the African maid walked in and began, with a great rattle of plates, to clear away. The Senhora heaved herself to her feet, once again just a heavily built, lethargic, elderly woman, not even bothering to glance at Kate as she said:

'The hour of the siesta. Rosa will be already asleep and must not be disturbed. We will meet at tea—for the Englese must have their tea, must they not?' she finished.

Kate stood up and waited while the older woman left the room, then she stood still, looking at the dark sullen face of the maid who was deliberately avoiding her eyes, and wondered what to do.

Could she go out and explore the town? But Mr. Lister had said he would be round to see her that afternoon.

There seemed no solution but to go to her room, and as she walked down the corridor the quietness oppressed her. There was a musty smell in the air—she shivered despite the heat. If she had known where Rosa slept . . . yet after those words of the Senhora it was almost impossible to try to see the child. And besides, Kate could not open every door in the hope of finding the right bedroom. No—she must just be patient.

But it would not be easy.

CHAPTER III

It was very pleasant, sitting on the small balcony with that wonderful view before her, and Kate seized the chance to write a letter to her mother. It was always easy to write to her because Kate knew how much her letters meant, and so Kate's pen ran easily—but when she read the letter through again, she was horrified.

Put down in black and white, it made a terrible story. Of a frightened small child, her possessive and resentful relatives—an arrival so very different from what they had expected. The words even painted Randel Lister as the type of man who was too busy to care about making Kate's arrival easy . . .

Kate read the letter through again and then tore it up. Feeling she was being very melodramatic, she found matches and burned the pieces. Then she wrote another letter. This one was much more cheerful, mentioning Mrs. McCormack's wonderful son, James, who had proved even nicer than his mother had said; the lovely view from the balcony, the excited feeling in the air of this unusual town—the charm of small Rosa . . .

Kate jumped to her feet as she heard the click-clacking of high heels in the corridor through the half-open door. Then she heard a door open and a deep voice. She was by the door already and only just stopped in time as she heard Randel Lister say:

'Why, Mariana—how very charming you look!'

Kate froze, holding her breath. And a deep, seductively husky voice replied, 'Randel—she is here, that one.' The voice was tragic, hurt. 'Randel—this is something that I do not comprehend. How can you do this to me? I love Rosa like my own *bébé*—you take her from me!' Her voice rose slightly and then fell. 'Ah, Randel . . .' There was a pause, and Kate could imagine Mariana's appealing face gazing up at the tall man. Then Mariana seemed to lose patience, as if he was not responding as he should. 'You will give her this so ordinary English mees,' she finished scornfully.

Not sure what to do, Kate stood still. She was tempted to walk out, but they might think she had been listening. Also it might embarrass Mr. Lister. Yet she dare not move lest they hear her.

When Mr. Lister spoke, it was in a patient voice. 'My dear Mariana, we have already been over this a dozen times. I thought you had accepted the situation—' Kate caught her breath as she listened. Had Mr. Lister expected her to handle it all alone? Surely he could see that Mariana had *not* accepted the situation and had no intention of doing so?

Mariana changed her voice again. Now she

was dramatic. 'You do not trust me? Me . . . How can you be so cruel, Randel? All these years, we loved Rosa as our own. Indeed she is our own. She is so healthy . . .'

'Much too pale and thin,' he said in an irritable voice.

'Randel!' Mariana sounded heartbroken. 'How can you say such a wicked thing? What child in a tropical land is anything but pale? How can she sit in the heat of the sun without shelter? She would soon be ill with the sun-madness. You tell us she is too quiet and too good. Is that not the biggest foolishness of all? Is it bad for a child to behave well? Indeed—you English, as they say, are all mad.'

'Well, my dear Mariana, they do say, "Mad dogs and Englishmen" . . .' Mr. Lister sounded amused. Kate wondered if he was used to Mariana's scenes and took no account of them.

'My little Rosa—' Mariana tried again. *'Ela e feliz.'* This was one of the phrases Kate knew. She felt like rushing out and calling Mariana a liar. Kate knew very well that the child was not happy. How could she be when she was so afraid?

Now Mariana's voice changed again; it trembled, her English deteriorated. Maybe she thought it more attractive. Kate was shocked at her own cattiness, but she was beginning to dislike Mariana intensely, even though she had not yet met her.

'It ees all too deefficult . . . It weel nevaire worrk . . .'

'Mariana—nothing is too difficult. In a few days, you will wonder how you managed without Kate. You will be free—able to go out more happily . . .' He sounded amused, as if he was being sarcastic. 'By the way, will you tell Kate I want to see her?'

Mr. Lister spoke as if the whole matter had been settled and there was no need for further discussion. Kate wondered if it could be as simple as that. And then her anger grew again as she heard Mariana say scornfully:

'She is asleep, that one. Her first day at work and she must sleep. I am not to have the disturbance, she said . . .'

It was all Kate could do not to rush out. What a wicked lie! But even as she weighed up the disadvantages of being caught out eavesdropping and the opportunity to tell Mr. Lister the truth, Mariana spoke again.

'You have no heart, Randel. Can you not see that everyone, they will laugh at me? If you had said you wished Rosa to be an English child, I would have made her one. I am telling you that, my Randel . . .' She paused, and Kate heard Randel's amused laugh. Mariana went on, obviously angry. 'You have no heart at all. You come here—but not to see me. Once on a time, it was me you longed to see, to love. You wish to see that one now—good, then you will see how very stupid you have been. But let her

54

have her sleep—and let us talk for a while . . .'

'Look, Mariana, I'm very busy and I want to see Kate Williams.'

'Please . . . please, Randel. It ees not too much to ask,' Mariana pleaded.

Kate heard a door open and close and there was silence. She went slowly back to gaze at the sea—this time angrily. What sort of man was Randel Lister if such a girl as Mariana could twist him so easily round her finger? Maybe it was what sort of a girl was Mariana that she should ask, Kate thought. James had said how beautiful she was . . .

Sitting there, listening intently, Kate faced the future unhappily. If Mariana could so easily influence Mr. Lister, everything would be doubly hard. Obviously, as Mrs. Kelly had prophesied, the Dominguez resented Kate and saw her as an obstacle to be removed. Having Mr. Lister's confidence, they would probably be successful.

Kate sighed. It wasn't the job now that mattered. She had enjoyed the voyage and her fare home would be paid. But now the job, as a job, no longer really existed—it was Rosa who mattered. Somehow or other Kate knew that she must find a way to outwit the Dominguez—to turn Rosa into a happy little girl, a normal child.

She stood up and went indoors, brushing her honey-blonde hair until it gleamed, carefully making up her full, generous mouth, running a finger along her eyebrows. She peered at herself. No beauty—but a fresh young face. The sort of face you would like a girl to have if she was looking after your child. After all, that was how Mr. Lister saw her, wasn't it? She need not even have the tiniest hope that he saw her as an attractive woman.

When she heard a door open, she was down the corridor in a moment.

'I wasn't asleep, Mr. Lister,' she began. 'I was waiting for you.'

Randel Lister was facing her, looking just as she remembered him. Tall, very well dressed in a dark suit, with a gardenia in the buttonhole. He held his head with the same air of arrogance, his eyes were cool and shrewd as he looked at her, then he half turned, and Kate saw Mariana.

It was then Kate came down to brass tacks and faced facts.

How could she win?

How could any man doubt Mariana, once he had gazed into the heart-shaped, olive face with those intense dark eyes, incredible lashes and that full, passionate, provocative mouth? Tall and slim, she looked too wonderful for words to describe in a sheath frock of deep coral.

No wonder James—and everyone else— wondered how Randel Lister could resist her! And what hope had Kate of making him believe her if Mr. Lister had to choose between them?

She caught her breath as he came down the corridor, speaking cheerfully. 'Ah, Kate, settled in all right?'

Kate thought it sounded too cheerful, and wondered what arrangements Mariana had wheedled out of him. Maybe she had suggested that Kate be on a month's trial— maybe only a week. Whatever it was, they would make it as hard as they could, and Kate knew that the one thing she needed more than anything else to win Rosa's confidence was— time.

Mr. Lister was introducing her to Mariana. 'This is Kate Williams, and I'm sure you will find her a great help. Kate, this is Mariana Dominguez. I hope you two girls will become good friends.'

Kate stared at him and then at the beautiful Portuguese girl, and saw in her face the same amusement at the utter foolishness of men. Kate also saw in Mariana's eyes the same suspicion she knew must be in her own, and for a moment felt swift sympathy with the lovely girl. If Mariana really loved Randel Lister, then this must be a bitter pill to swallow. But did she? James had implied that Mariana was selfish and that Randel already knew this, and that this was the reason for his hesitation. The next second, Kate lost all sympathy for Mariana, whose eyes hardened as she said frostily,

'It ees not easy for Eenglese and Portuguese girls to be friends. We have deeferent standards.'

Kate's cheeks went bright red with anger and she noticed how swiftly Mr. Lister intervened.

'Of course you have. All nationalities differ—that's what makes it so interesting to meet people from other lands.' He stared at Mariana's cold face and Kate saw an odd look on his face—amusement, resignation, and something she thought looked like acceptance. Then he turned to Kate and she saw his face change again, become cloaked, impersonal, very polite. 'Have you met Rose?'

Mariana spoke quickly, giving Kate no time to answer. 'It was not a success,' she said sadly, spreading out her hands expressively.

Kate, her cheeks still flushed, said, 'We could hardly expect her to like me at sight. She is bound to see me as a stranger, at first.'

But Mr. Lister was staring at her, frowning. 'That's odd. I would have thought . . .' He hesitated.

Kate, glancing sideways, saw the triumph on Mariana's face. How Kate wished that the wretched girl would go away and leave them alone. How could she make Mr. Lister understand the gravity of the situation with Mariana waiting to interrupt at any moment, able—and without the slightest effort—to divert and attract, as well as hold, his whole attention? Kate took a deep breath.

'Mr. Lister,' she said with all the dignity her nineteen years could muster. 'You must understand that this will not be easy. Rosa has never met me before—we were barely allowed time to speak to one another. What hope had I of making friends in that time?' She could see that Mariana was beginning to speak, so she raised her voice and spoke faster. 'I don't think it's fair of you to expect me to become friends when I'm not even allowed to be alone with the child.'

There was an appalled silence. Mr. Lister stared at her, his eyes disbelieving. 'But that's . . .'

'Nonsense?' Kate's cheeks were burning now, her voice raised still more. 'I assure you it's not nonsense, Mr. Lister. When I arrived, Rosa was out.'

'Rose,' he said irritably.

She bit her lip and, glancing at Mariana, decided to let him have the point, temporarily. 'Rose,' she went on, 'was out for a walk. When she came in, I saw her for a few moments, and . . .'

'She ran away screaming,' Mariana put in hastily, her voice malicious.

Randel Lister gazed from one to the other of the girls anxiously, still frowning. For a brief second Kate was sorry for him. But she was even sorrier for Rosa. She went on: 'That is true. Something had been said to frighten her.

59

I barely said *Hullo* to her and told her my name. She ran away screaming. I wanted to go after her—to talk to her, but I was not allowed to see her again. She did not eat with us—and afterwards Anna put her to bed. I have not seen her since. I don't think, Mr. Lister, that it's fair to blame me for not having made friends with her,' she finished breathlessly.

She saw that she might just as well have held her tongue. Mariana had tucked her hand through his arm, and was leaning lightly against him, smiling. And Mr. Lister was looking at Kate with distaste on his face. 'I think you must be very tired to be so hysterical,' he said coldly. 'That is a very different story from what I have already heard. I think if you go to bed early and have a good rest, the situation will appear completely different.' He gave her a card. 'This is my office address in town. I shall expect to see you tomorrow at eleven o'clock, when we can discuss the matter more fully. You will need to buy your clothes. I expect you're finding it hot . . .'

His voice had softened, and Kate wondered if the dismay and shock she was feeling was visible on her face. She felt as if the ground had been cut away beneath her feet. He did not believe her. He had no intention of believing her. Already he was accepting Mariana's lies and not giving Kate a chance to prove them false. She caught her breath, feeling the tears suddenly near, longing with all her heart for her mother's brisk sympathy, for her advice. What would her mother have said? *Battle to the end, darling, but don't let them see you're hurt.* Now she forced a smile on her face and said politely,

'I am, a little.'

'You have a comfortable room?' he asked with equal formality.

'Yes, thank you. I have the most heavenly view.'

Mr. Lister looked relieved. Kate had a feeling he was shirking the issue and knew it, and was a little ashamed of his own behaviour. It made her feel sorry for him again. Maybe it was not easy for a man—especially if he loved someone like Mariana.

Now he turned away. 'Good, I'll see you tomorrow, then. Rose may be used to you and . . .' He stopped, for Mariana had lifted his hand and was holding it to her cheek, smiling at him through her long lashes.

'Randel—my Randel . . .' she said softly. And then began to talk to him in Portuguese. It sounded so liquid, so lovely that Kate's throat tightened for a moment. It sounded like . . . like a love song. Watching Mr. Lister's face, Kate guessed that it was probably that—just that. Mariana was obviously pleading, teasing him, and finally getting what she wanted. Then she smiled, looking quickly at Kate with a triumphant smile, and said, 'Ah—I knew you

61

would agree, my Randel.' She looked directly at Kate and said, 'Tell my mother, mees, that I shall be late tonight.'

Kate stood still, watching them go. Mr. Lister had said goodbye rather abruptly, and had looked ill at ease. He had said he was busy, yet he was taking Mariana out somewhere—somewhere that was a good way away if they were going to be late that night.

Miserably, she went back to her bedroom. Round Number Two to the Dominguez, she thought unhappily. She took off her dress, drew the curtains and lay on her bed, feeling the hot tears burning her eyes. She tried not to cry; maybe he was right and she was very tired. Actually she felt utterly exhausted. Everything was so different from what she expected. What would her mother have said? It was obvious that Mr. Lister did not live with the Dominguez—but surely he had a governess for his little girl, and if he had a real desire to make her English, he would have Rosa and Kate to live in his house? Kate turned over, burying her face in the pillow, wishing with all her heart that Mr. Lister had never gone to Mr. Stowe's and so walked into her life. And she remembered Rosa . . . and was glad that he had.

CHAPTER IV

When Kate woke, she heard music. Dressing hurriedly, she went in search of it and found the Senhora sitting alone, still embroidering, and listening to the radio. Her dark, forbidding face turned towards Kate.

'Yes, mees?'

Kate repeated Mariana's message and saw the Senhora's face come alive with pleasure. 'Ah—but that is good.' Then her face went blank again. 'Doubtless you will find something with which to interest yourself.'

Kate stared at her. 'Where is Rose—Rosa?'

The Senhora bent over her needlework. She did not even bother to look up as she answered, 'She has gone for her walk as usual.'

Kate stood there and there was silence from the Portuguese woman, even though she waited until the silence became embarrassing. Then Kate turned away and left the room, feeling both furious and completely helpless. How could she combat such a campaign? If she was never allowed to see the child . . .

She stared miserably at the sea and then thought of something. She went back and told the Senhora she was going for a walk and hurried down the stairs to the hall. The girl she had seen before was entering figures in a ledger. When she looked up and saw Kate, she

63

smiled. 'I am Natala Viera,' she said politely.

'I am Kate Williams,' Kate said, and went down to her. Kate added out of her bitterness, 'It's nice to find someone who will talk to me.'

She recognised the comprehension and compassion on Natala's face. 'Ah, Mees Williams, I am afraid it is not easy for you,' Natala said gently.

Kate took a deep breath and managed a smile. 'You're right it isn't. I say, do call me Kate, and may I call you Natala? What a pretty name it is.'

For a second Natala's face glowed with pleasure. Kate wondered if it was her first compliment. Natala gave her the impression of being very sensitive and sad.

'I thank you very much. I will be happy to call you Kate.' She pronounced it *'Ket,'* and somehow it made it sound pretty and no longer sensible. 'I, too, am lonely.'

'That's wrong—why, you're young and—' Kate began.

Natala moved her hand a little. 'People stare at me—they pity me, and are then ashamed. They are not at ease.' She searched for a word and Kate waited. 'I am an embarrassment,' she finished sadly.

'Not to me,' Kate told her. 'You need lots of courage and I admire you for it. You're a spastic, aren't you?' Kate went on as Natala nodded. 'At the hospital where I trained as a children's nurse there was a spastic department. I knew a lot of children like it, and I know how very difficult life can be.'

Natala beamed. 'Oh, you cannot know how good it is to have someone speak about it so openly. They whisper. They look, and then look away, as if . . . as if I was a—a leper.'

'They must be poor types,' Kate finished flatly. 'Anyone with any education or intelligence recognises that spastics can be helped a great deal today and that everything depends on their own courage and endurance. They ought to admire you—as I do.' She spoke sincerely and was glad to see the girl look happier. A warm rush of affection filled Kate. She put her hand on Natala's. 'I need a friend, Natala. Will you be mine?'

Natala's fingers curled round Kate's. 'Oh, thank you! Yes, please,' she said softly.

After that they chatted for a while, both avoiding the subject of her job. Kate guessed Natala was being tactful—but she herself was hesitating because she felt it was disloyal to her employer to discuss him. Finally Kate said she thought she might go exploring.

'Rosa has gone out and I wondered what to do. I can't just sit in my bedroom all day.' Even as she spoke, Kate wondered why she had not thought of it before. 'I'll telephone Mrs. McCormack,' she decided.

As Natala got the number for her, Kate told her a little about her shipboard friend. 'She was wonderful to me, so kind.'

Natala's eyes were bright. 'I think that it would be easy to be kind to you,' she said a little shyly.

As Kate took the telephone, she smiled at her new friend. 'I wish other people thought the same,' she said.

It was wonderful to hear Mrs. McCormack's voice—just like going home. It was easy to find the house, Kate thought as she walked down the road, glad of the shade of the trees planted either side.

Villa Paradis, where the McCormacks lived, was a large white building with a wide patio and a balcony above it. The tiled garden had wide beds of gay flowers. It was just the sort of house Kate had mentally pictured Randel Lister living in.

Even before she could touch the bell, the front door was flung open and there was Mrs. McCormack, looking cool and comfortable in a loose silk blue frock. She almost took Kate in her arms, crying eagerly:

'But this is lovely, my dear. I never hoped to hear from you so soon.'

It was a beautiful house, a heavenly house to live in, Kate thought at once. Large airy rooms were filled with soft draperies and jars of flowers; there were light wicker, surprisingly comfortable armchairs. The shining floors were scattered with deep crimson and blue rugs. Kate and Mrs. McCormack sat talking, with long golden ice-cold drinks that soothed

66

Kate's dry throat.

Kate had not had time to prepare what she was going to tell Mrs. McCormack, though she had vaguely intended not telling her the whole truth—but Mrs. McCormack was one of those people who seem to get every detail out of you without effort.

As the words poured out of Kate's mouth, she watched, on Mrs. McCormack's face, all those conflicting emotions she had felt that day surprise, dismay, disbelief, amusement, shock—disappointment.

'Well,' Mrs. McCormack said finally. 'You have surprised me. I would have thought Mr. Lister was a man of far greater discernment than that. I feel, my dear, that he has behaved extremely badly. Whatever happened, he should have introduced you to the Dominguez and to his daughter. That would have made the situation plain from the beginning.'

'He had an appointment,' Kate put in, a little dismayed that she had apparently painted Mr. Lister in such a bad light.

'So had you,' Mrs. McCormack said dryly. 'A far more important appointment where the child is concerned. Then—then he must surely appreciate that the Dominguez family resent you, even if he, somewhat stupidly, hoped they would not.'

She wanted to know about the little girl, and was as shocked as Kate had been by the child's obvious fear. 'Yet, Kate dear, I see it as a very good sign that the child sought you out of her own accord. It seems to me that her curiosity about you may be your best weapon. As you say, you must go slowly.'

Later, Mrs. McCormack said thoughtfully, 'Kate, maybe we're making a mountain out of the proverbial molehill. Men can be such fools, and obviously Randel Lister won't see two inches beyond his nose if he doesn't want to. When you see him tomorrow, you *must* be more businesslike.' She smiled at the quiet, tired unhappy girl—the girl who appeared so different from the happy Kate of the ship. 'My dear, I know it isn't easy at nineteen to stand up to a cosmopolitan, experienced, perhaps sarcastic man.' Her eyes twinkled sympathetically at Kate's quick denial. 'Yes, dear, I do understand that it was very hot and he had a busy day and that we must make allowances. At the same time, you must stand up for yourself, or the Dominguez will just crush you with . . . with steamroller precision.' Mrs. McCormack beamed for a moment. Kate knew how the older woman loved what she called an 'apt phrase.'

'But how?' Kate asked, rather helplessly, remembering Mr. Lister's cold eyes, that look of distaste that still seemed to shrivel her up as she remembered it.

'He must define your duties. Make him see that you appreciate that it's difficult for the Dominguez to accept you. That it's difficult for you living under their roof. Ask him to make it plain that, now you are here, the girl Anna is redundant.' She beamed again. 'That's a good word to remember, my dear. Redundant. I'm sure if you make him see how impossible the situation is, he will respond. After all, he *did* engage you to look after the child.'

Later, as Kate prepared to leave—for she did not like to stay away too long, although the thought of going back to that gloomy flat was terrifying—Mrs. McCormack told Kate that Randel Lister lived at the Aviz Hotel and had never taken a villa because of his frequent absences. But that she imagined that now, things would be different. Kate wondered what James had told his mother as Mrs. McCormack continued: 'I happen to know that he is staying in Lourenço Marques for the next six months and so he may rent a furnished villa. That would be the most sensible plan, for then you and the child could be with him.'

'That would be wonderful,' Kate said eagerly, and then wondered if she had been just a little too eager as she saw Mrs. McCormack's shrewd eyes on her. She coloured and said hastily, 'It's so dark and dingy in that flat. Also it isn't easy with the Dominguez disliking me so and . . . and making everything so hard.' She thought of something, hoping it would distract Mrs. McCormack's attention. It did. 'Mariana,' Kate said, 'is very lovely.'

'So James says. Tell me about her.'

Kate tried to obey. It was difficult to capture Mariana's fiery beauty, her husky voice, those compelling eyes, that seductive manner, the rather possessive way she spoke to Mr. Lister one moment, and the next was appealing, begging, almost like a slave.

'Is he in love with her?' Mrs. McCormack made that emotional state sound like a disease.

'I don't know,' Kate said. 'I don't see how he could fail to be. She is really . . . really most exceptional.' How inadequate words were! 'She has such personality as well as beauty. Such arrogance . . . self-confidence. When she looks at me I feel just like a country mouse.'

Mrs. McCormack looked disapproving. 'You look just what you are—a well brought up young English girl.'

Kate smiled a little. 'How dull and boring that sounds! I think it must be wonderful to look like Mariana.'

'Maybe,' Mrs. McCormack said with a little sniff and that habit of hers of always having the last word. 'But remember that Mr. Lister engaged *you* to look after his child.'

The words sent Kate back to the Pensao Fadora with renewed courage. It was true. He had engaged her. And tomorrow they would discuss the whole matter and find a solution.

Natala was not in the hall of the Pensio, and Kate felt sorry for that, for her confidence

70

began to vanish as she climbed the stairs slowly. As she passed the open sitting-room door, the Senhora looked up. She was still sitting in the same high-backed chair, her flat-heeled shoes resting on the embroidered footstool, still sewing.

'You will join me, mees.'

It was an order. Kate reluctantly entered the room and then rang the bell as directed. She sat on a chair and the two women gazed at one another while a tray of coffee and rich cream cakes arrived. Not liking to risk the Senhora's anger, Kate ate one cake while the Senhora enjoyed four, then they drank two cups of very sweet coffee.

It was then that the front door opened and Kate heard a child's voice. Instantly she stood up, determined not to lose her chance this time.

'Rosa! I'd better—'

But the Senhora waved an imperative hand. 'Sit down,' she said harshly. 'I tell you, mees, sit down.'

There was so much anger in the voice that Kate obeyed. She sat down and stared at the older woman and the hopelessness of the situation pervaded her body. How could she fight?

'Leave the child to Anna. It is better so.' Now the Senhora's voice was less angry, as if she was surprised at Kate's obedience. She even smiled at Kate—if that creaking stiff

71

grimace could be called a smile. 'She knows Anna, and you are a stranger,' she finished contemptuously.

Kate took a deep breath and found courage to protest. 'But, Senhora,' she said in a very mild voice. 'If I do nothing for Rosa, how can she ever know me?'

The black beady eyes were mocking as the Senhora stared at Kate. 'It will come, in time,' she said.

Kate looked down at her hands, which were twisting together unconsciously as she tried to control herself. What did the Senhora mean by *it*? Her friendship with the child? Or, more likely, her dismissal? Was that what they were counting on—proving to Mr. Lister that Kate was an absolute fool? That she had failed to make a contact of any sort with the child? Or were they going to drive her into handing in her resignation? Were they going to frustrate her at every turn—force her into making complaints, annoying and antagonising Mr. Lister, and so strengthening their position? Were they planning to make her so miserable that she had to leave?

Kate looked up and smiled politely. 'You're right,' she said meekly.

This was something that had to be fought—and fight it she would, she thought, letting her eyes fall demurely, thinking of what Mrs. McCormack had said. This was something she must do for Rosa's sake.

The evening dragged by with seeming endlessness. The Senhora told her when it was time to bath and change for dinner. Fortunately the bath water was hot, and despite the humidity of the evening Kate enjoyed that part. She dressed slowly, longing to know in which room Rosa slept, yet knowing she could do nothing about it. She ate alone with the Senhora, who ploughed her way solidly and silently through six courses while Kate nibbled at her food, unable now to enjoy it because of the emotions that were surging inside her. While she tried to look subdued and meek, inwardly she was rebelling, planning ahead, hanging on to her courage, counting the hours until the next morning when she would see Randel Lister.

It was when Kate had given up all hope of seeing Rosa that day that she had her chance and seized it. After dinner, as she walked down to her room, she heard a strange tune and guessed it was Anna, singing Rosa a lullaby. Very quickly—and before she could change her mind—Kate knocked on the door and opened it.

Rosa was in bed. She sat up at once, eyes wide with fright.

'Anna!' she exclaimed.

The plump African girl whom Kate had seen before moved quickly to Rosa's side, saying something in a soft voice, turning to stare at Kate with angry, fearful, defiant eyes.

Kate stood still in dismay. Rosa was afraid of her. Oh, why had she taken a chance and walked into the room? Why hadn't she been patient just a while longer?

'I came to say good night, Rosa. Please teach me to say it in Portuguese,' Kate said very gently.

'Boa noite,' Rosa said, her voice trembling, her body stiff with fear.

'Thank you,' Kate managed to say as she fought the sudden desire to cry—cry with annoyance and anger at her own folly; to cry—with pity for the child. *'Boa noite. Obrigado, Rosa, boa noite.' As* she turned away and left the room she saw Rosa fling her arms round the African girl's neck.

Kate stood on the balcony of her room for a long time until the mosquitoes began to bite her. Then she went into the hot, airless room, leaving the window open but closing the wire netting. She stood still, staring at nothing, tasting the bitterness of defeat.

Yet, with the resilience of youth, when she awoke next morning and saw the sun shining on the shimmering blue glory of the Indian Ocean her spirits lifted. The birds were twittering shrilly in the trees and, suddenly, all was right with her world. She could remember Mrs. McCormack's words of advice, remember that in England Mr. Lister had shown great concern for his child. He must surely understand—somehow she must make him.

74

Anna was in the dining-room, laying the table, and Kate greeted her cheerfully, *'Bom dias.'*

Anna gave her a dark resentful look and went silently out of the room, her bare pink-soled black feet moving lightly over the polished floor. The flat was very quiet, and Kate wondered if she had risen too early, so went back to her room, standing on the balcony to watch a big white liner coming slowly and gracefully into dock, just as Kate's had done, the previous day.

The previous day.

Kate gasped as she took in the significance of the words. Had she only been in Lourenço Marques for one day? It seemed unbelievable —she had experienced so many different emotions—misery, excitement, alarm, and again, uncertainty. No wonder she felt as if she had been there for months. And wasn't it rather silly to feel a failure after such a short time? How melodramatic could she get? Maybe it was the heat, she thought. Already the sun's warmth was beating on to her.

She went down the corridor when the gong sounded and found that she was to eat alone. It seemed like being sent to Coventry—a habit of schooldays she had always thought the height of cruelty for a sensitive child—as she sat there, eating the tender slice of pressed beef served with a pungent sauce, followed by bacon and eggs, crisp rolls and butter. She had

75

no appetite and sat staring in front of her, drinking bitter coffee, and her misery grew as she thought ahead.

She must not let the Dominguez know how much she minded. Yet she did mind very much when she went to Rosa's room again and found the narrow bed made and the tiny room neat and no sign of Rosa anywhere.

Kate looked round, and her heart ached for the child. What a dreadful room, with its sombre curtains and dark heavy furniture. Kate's fingers itched to paint the walls pale pink, to put a gay cover on the bed, hang curtains with animals in the design, put bright rugs on the floor. How could Rosa be anything but fearful in such a gloomy atmosphere? And the curtains were so thick that at night, when they were drawn, not even a tiny chink of light would be able to creep through.

Kate carefully dressed for the forthcoming interview. As she was obviously not going to be allowed to see Rosa, she thought she might as well go down to the town and explore it a little before she saw Mr. Lister. It was as she went into the hall that she saw Mariana, wearing a trailing shabby transparent black housecoat, her black hair pinned in curls, her face sallow and drab without make-up. Kate wondered if Mr. Lister would still love Mariana if he could see her like that. But she knew that he probably would, for somehow—and maddeningly —Mariana managed to remain beautiful.

76

'I trust you had the good night, mees,' Mariana said sweetly.

'Yes, thank you,' Kate replied politely, wishing with all her heart that they would stop calling her 'mees.' The way Mariana and her mother said it made it sound like an insult.

Mariana gave her a brilliant smile. 'So did I—but not a long sleep, alas. It was so very late when the Senhor Lister brought me home. We danced, and he could not bear to let me return.'

Kate's face felt stiff. 'I'm glad that you both enjoyed yourselves,' she said, still very politely. Her hand closed convulsively. She knew very well what Mariana was telling her. But apparently Mariana was not sure that Kate fully understood.

'I am sure you are,' Mariana went on, still smiling, but her eyes were hard. 'The Senhor Lister and I—we have known one another a very long time. We are happy together. We are—' She held up one hand and straightened the first two fingers together so that they were joined and, apparently, one finger. 'We are like that—you understand?'

'I understand,' Kate said. She tried to pass Mariana and caught a glimpse of herself in the mirror. She wondered why Mariana bothered to warn her to leave Mr. Lister alone. What would he ever see in that ordinary-looking face with the fair curly hair and good skin? Just a pleasant-looking face . . .

77

But—Kate remembered suddenly—Mrs. McCormack had pointed out that he had engaged Kate to look after his daughter, and not Mariana.

That was something she must hang on to when things got too bad. Now, after she had passed Mariana and let herself out of the flat, she hurried downstairs with a feeling of escaping from something very ugly.

Natala greeted her warmly and told her how to get to town and where to catch the bus. She even gave Kate some Portuguese money for the fare.

And then, as Kate was leaving, Natala smiled and said, 'I keep the fingers crossed—so!' She lifted one hand, showing her crossed fingers to Kate and smiling. 'That means good luck for you when you meet Mr. Lister—is it not so?'

'Thanks, Natala,' Kate said, trying to sound cheerful. 'Thanks a lot—I'll need it,' she said, and smiled. But as she hurried to the bus stop she wondered how Natala had known that she had an appointment with Mr. Lister.

CHAPTER V

Kate had no difficulty finding the bus stop, and she enjoyed the ride down town, for now she could look around her and appreciate the blinding sunshine and the pure white of the buildings, with their gay window-boxes and gardens. When she left the bus she walked down the main shopping street and felt as if she were walking on air. Everything looked different—the shops, the people, the traffic. Such huge cars were sliding noiselessly by— and then one impatiently honking as a cyclist swung carelessly across his path. She found the address Mr. Lister had given her, saw his name RANDEL LISTER on the board in the hall under AFRICO-AMERIC COMPANY. Looking at her watch, she found she only had a few moments in hand, so she got into the lift, which shot her up to the thirteenth floor.

As a very pretty girl with a pony-tail of black silky hair came to ask her her business, Kate realised that she should have rehearsed what she had to say to her employer. Even as the girl went away with Kate's name to find out if Mr. Lister would see her, Kate tried to remember all the things Mrs. McCormack had told her.

Her duties must be defined. The Dominguez must understand that she was to look after Rosa. Anna was redundant.

But was she?

The girl returned and led Kate to Mr. Lister's office. Kate had just time to get an impression of huge lofty rooms, great windows letting in the light and a number of young men and girls sitting at desks, and then she was alone with Mr. Lister.

He did not look up. He sat at a big lightwood desk, bent over some papers. Kate hesitated, noting what long fingers he had and how rapidly he wrote, without hesitation, as if he knew exactly what he intended to say. Then he looked up.

Kate met the full impact of his searching, demanding, sceptical gaze. She took a deep breath and clutched her handbag more tightly, trying not to let him see just how shaken she always was when she was near him.

It was absurd. He was her employer. He saw her as a pleasant, rather dull, but safe English girl who might be able to help his daughter— might now being the operative word.

Yet she still had this sense of breathless excitement when she was in the same room with him, the feeling of expectancy, of something wonderful about to happen.

Pure nonsense, of course. What she probably was going to get was the sack!

That gave her courage. 'Good morning, Mr. Lister,' she said coolly.

He got up then, settled her in a chair,

offered and lighted a cigarette, then sat opposite her and smiled at her. But it was a cool, calculating smile, and she felt the palms of her hands go damp. So Mariana *had* talked him into some arrangement!

A silence fell between them and they stared at one another. Kate had read somewhere that, when being interviewed, it is always wise to leave the other person to do all the talking—it gives you the advantage. Maybe Mr. Lister had read the same article, for the silence grew between them until it became quite embarrassing. Kate sighed and capitulated.

'Mr. Lister,' she said very formally, 'I must talk to you about the position I'm in.'

He leant back in his chair, flexing his fingers and half smiling. 'Well?' he asked.

Neither the question nor the voice was very helpful. Kate took another deep breath. 'Mr. Lister, I'm in a very difficult position,' she began again, and realised she was repeating herself and getting nowhere.

Then he smiled, and she caught her breath. Had any other man in the world such a thrilling, completely disarming smile? All her anger vanished, and she could see his side of the question instead of her own.

'Kate—I appreciate that,' he said slowly, 'but then so am I.' He spread out his hands in a little foreign gesture which, she thought unhappily, he must have caught from Mariana.

'The Dominguez—they have been so good to Rose and me. I hadn't realised that this would hurt them so much. If I'd known . . .' He paused, and Kate could hear her own heart beating as she waited.

When he did not continue, but went on looking at her with that vaguely sad smile, she knew what she must do. Bending her head so that he should not see the disappointment in her eyes, she said in a small voice:

'I understand. You feel it would be better if I went back to England.'

She was startled by the violence of his protest. 'Of course I have no such thought!' He glared at her as if she had said something wicked. 'Or are you regretting taking the job?' he asked scornfully.

Anger was always a good tonic for Kate. Now her cheeks reddened and her eyes flashed. 'Of course I'm not. I want to stay on— I want to look after your daughter, but everything that has happened so far has led me to believe that you've changed your mind about the situation and want Maria . . .' She stopped and began again. 'Want the Dominguez to continue to take care of her.'

The anger had left Mr. Lister's face. 'What has made you think that?'

She was no longer afraid of him. 'Do you want me to tell you the truth?' she asked.

Perhaps her solemnity was amusing, though she did not find it so, for now he was half

82

smiling again. She forced her eyes away from his lean, attractive face and concentrated her thoughts on the things that must be said.

'Yes, please,' Mr. Lister told her. 'The whole truth and nothing but the truth.' She could hear from his voice that he was smiling, but she refused to look at him.

Her face was stiff and her voice a little unsteady as she obeyed. Not looking at him, she had no idea how he was reacting as he heard the account of her first meeting with the child, of Rosa's terror, of the Senhora's insistence that Kate leave the child to Anna, of her attempts to make friends with the child— and that the greatest obstacle she had to face was his daughter's fear of her.

She looked down at her hands, twisting her fingers together unhappily. 'You see, Mr. Lister, this isn't something I can do in a few hours. Your daughter has only known the Dominguez and Anna. I am a stranger and . . . I'm afraid she has . . . has been led to believe that with me life will be—well, not very pleasant. If you could see how afraid she is of me, how she clings to Anna

'She's afraid of *you?*' Mr. Lister asked slowly.

Kate ventured to look at him. There was shock and anger on his face but, for once, no disbelief. He leaned forward.

'Can you account for that?' he asked.

Kate hesitated. What a very awkward

situation it was! It was difficult to find diplomatic yet truthful words.

'Mr. Lister—it can't be easy for the Senhora to have me come out here. Old people find it hard to adjust themselves. Anna, too, probably thinks it means she will no longer be wanted, and she seems very fond of Rosa.'

'Why do you keep calling her Rosa?' Mr. Lister put in irritably. 'Her name is Rose.'

Kate stared at him. 'But she has been called Rosa all her life. That, to her, is her name. How would you like it . . . if someone started calling you Dick?'

She was startled by his shout of laughter. '*Touché!*' he said. 'Go on.'

Kate still hesitated. She began pleating the soft material of her frock.

'It won't be very easy for me, Mr. Lister, unless the Dominguez are willing to accept me. At the moment I feel an intruder, an unwanted nuisance.' Against her will, her voice shook. 'You do see how hard it is for me to gain Rosa's confidence unless she feels that her grandmother and . . . that her grandmother approved of me. If they treat me as an alien, unwanted, resented, she is bound to feel the same emotions towards me.'

Looking at Mr. Lister, she saw that he was nodding, his face grave. 'I blame myself entirely for this unfortunate situation,' he said slowly. 'I had not, as I just said, realised the depths of their love for the child—nor that they would be so hurt. However, as I plan to send Rose to boarding school when we go to England—' He stopped. 'What are you looking like that for?' he said sharply. 'I told you I was only engaging you for six months.'

Kate tried to recover her composure; she knew that her face had showed dismay and shock. Then she found courage. 'I was just being sorry for Rosa,' she explained. 'Just as she gets used to me, she will have to get used to a totally new life. Boarding school is all right for some people, but—'

She saw by the anger in his eyes that she had gone too far, and waited for the explosion. Instead he said coldly:

'Considering that you've spoken about four words to my daughter, you appear to take an excessive interest in her welfare.'

That made her angry again. 'Of course I do. Any decent person would. Here is a child, deprived of her mother, barely knowing her father, brought up in one atmosphere, learning to be a good child, to please her elders—and suddenly she is expected to change completely both her behaviour and her manner, and then—in six months—will have to suffer another metamorphosis.' Kate stopped. Where on earth had she got that long word from? How Mrs. McCormack would have beamed! That reminded her of that kind woman, so she took another breath.

'Please, Mr. Lister, it's wrong of me to make

such a criticism. I apologise. It's just that—that it nearly broke my heart to have Rosa so frightened of me.' It was maddening, but her voice suddenly thickened. 'I've never had a child look at me like that before. I would give anything to see her happy.'

There was silence while she blew her nose, blinked her eyes and tried to regain her calm.

When Mr. Lister spoke, it was in a totally different voice.

'Thank you, Kate. I asked for that and deserved it. We must now do what we can to put this unfortunate situation right. Believe me, I *do* want my daughter to become an English child—as you say, to laugh, be naughty, happy, normal. I also agree that the Dominguez are making the situation needlessly difficult. We must accept that and realise that every nationality looks at each situation differently. No doubt that's one of the reasons that the world is always in such a mess.' He smiled at Kate and she felt herself relax, falling once again under his charm.

'What shall we do, Kate?'

He was appealing to her! Kate thought before she spoke. Then she said:

'First, I think it would help if you would let the Senhora know that you want me to look after the child, that I'm disobeying your orders if I don't do so.'

'I'll do that—and Anna must go.'

'Oh, no!' Kate cried in distress. 'No, that

86

would never do.'

He frowned for a moment. 'But that was one of the things you complained of—'

'Not that, exactly.' Kate's hands were twisting together again. This was her chance—she must not spoil it. 'I want to be allowed to *share* Rosa with Anna—I want to have meals with them, go for walks with them, let Anna teach me how to look after Rosa. I don't want Anna to be pushed out at all—or Rosa to feel that she is stranded with me and has no one to whom to turn.' Kate's young voice was grave as she tried to think wisely and talk at the same time. She looked anxiously at her employer.

'It won't be easy, Mr. Lister, but I think if I am very patient and can make both Rosa and Anna see that I'm a friend, I may win their confidence. It's just—just—' She hesitated, for this was really difficult. 'Would you make it clear that I take my orders from you?' She saw he was frowning at her.

'Mr. Lister—it's impossible to work for several masters.' Kate paused again. Neither of them had mentioned Mariana by name. That meant they both recognised, but dared not admit, that Mariana was the real stumbling-block. Kate sighed a little. How could she hope to fight Mariana?

'Mr. Lister, I promise I will be very diplomatic,' Kate borrowed one of Mrs. McCormack's pet expressions. 'I'll be the soul of discretion and will not willingly give them cause for anger.'

Perhaps it was the rather pedantic sentences or the look on Kate's face, but Mr. Lister was smiling at her again. 'I know that I can rely on you, Kate.' He looked at his watch. 'My dear girl, I had no idea—' He pulled out his wallet and gave her a wad of notes. 'Take the rest of the morning to do your shopping and buy some suitable clothes.' He screwed his eyes up as he smiled at her. 'Please look upon them as uniform and don't go counting the pennies. Only of course they're not pennies.' Kate could laugh with him now. 'You'll find the assistants very helpful about the different currency here. You need plenty of light frocks, Kate, if you and Rose are going for walks.' He stood up, and Kate rose too. 'Now, Kate, be back here by half-past twelve and I will drive you back to the flat, see the Senhora and make everything plain to her. Is that all right?'

Kate was thinking hard, clutching the wad of notes in her hand. She was startled when Mr. Lister put a firm finger under her chin and tilted her head back, making her look him in the eyes.

'Kate—' he said in a gentle voice. 'Don't you trust me?'

She swallowed and knew that she was trembling. She hoped he had not noticed and would never guess what an effect just the touch of one finger of his could have on her. 'I know it isn't easy for you,' she said.

He chuckled. 'How right you are, Kate.' He went with her to the door. 'I haven't got your courage nor your determination, I'm afraid.' As he opened the door, he smiled down at her again. 'Tell me, how is it that such a small person as you can be so aggressive?'

Kate looked up at him apologetically. 'Was I? I didn't mean to be, but I think when you're small, you have to make a lot of noise or people won't bother to listen to you.'

She could still hear his friendly laugh as she went to the lift. But it was nice laughter, warm, appreciative, friendly.

She went down in the lift feeling a great deal happier. Mr. Lister understood the situation, and that was half the battle. If only he could make the Dominguez accept her! Yet most of that must be done by herself—by her own attitude. She sighed a little. But still, it was a job worth doing, and she did have Mrs. McCormack to help her with encouragement —yes, and Natala, too.

Kate was smiling as the heat of the street hit her face scorchingly. She hurried over the street by the robot lights and was startled when someone stopped her on the island. She looked up and saw a tall young man with an olive skin.

'The English miss!' he said.

Kate frowned, and then recognised him as the man at the Pensao Fadora, the man who had stood too close and who had absurdly frightened her.

Now his hand was through her arm and he was crossing by her side. 'We will drink the coffee together,' he announced.

They had to pause on the pavement as a crocodile of demure-looking schoolgirls walked by, a serene-faced nun with them. Kate turned to look up at the tall building where Mr. Lister worked and carefully disengaged her arm from the young Portuguese's tight grasp. For a moment she thought she saw Mr. Lister standing in the window, but then the faint shadow moved and the windows stared blankly down. It had been silly even to look— why should he gaze down the street after her? Already he would be back at his desk, writing rapidly and with assurance, Kate and her troubles forgotten.

She turned to the young man and said firmly, 'I'm sorry, but I'm busy. I have shopping to do and then I have an appointment.'

He looked surprised. 'But just one leetle coffee . . . ?'

Kate smiled but firmly. 'I'm sorry, but no.'

He was saying. 'Another time, pliz?' as Kate hurried into one of the biggest shops and managed to lose him in the crowds.

CHAPTER VI

Kate had a wonderful time choosing light tropical clothes for her six months in Lourcnço Marques. As Mr. Lister had said, all the assistants were friendly, talking to her in English, and the time raced by so that she was quite breathless when she reached his office at the appointed hour.

He came to her as if in a great hurry, talking rather impatiently to the pretty girl with the dark pony-tail, and when they went down in the lift he hardly spoke to Kate. Kate, sitting by his side in the car, was content just to be there, and it hardly bothered her because his mood had changed again. Sympathetically she thought he was dreading the interview ahead, which might prove emotional.

It was odd how different things turn out to be, she thought later. The Senhora was all charm, her dark face broken by her nearest approach to a smile, her voice honeyed as she said finally:

'Ah but now I understand, Senhor. You wish Mees to spend her time with Rosa and the maid. That is good—if that is the way you wish it. To us, that would be—' she shrugged expressively, 'but the Englese, I know, are different.' She made it sound disparaging. 'It shall be as you wish it, Senhor Lister, as always.'

In the hall, Mr. Lister looked at Kate and half smiled.

'I hope that will help matters,' he said.

Kate hoped so, too. She smiled back. 'I'm sure it will,' she said with a great deal more confidence than she felt.

She had her first taste of Rosa and Anna's company immediately. Anna came to tell her lunch was ready and led her to a small dark room that was allotted to Rosa's waking hours. Feeling rather nervous, Kate sat down and began to eat. Rosa, who sat opposite her, was eating silently, her eyes huge and shadowed a little. Anna, the girl, marched heavily round the table, resentment in every movement. Kate decided not to talk but just to behave as though nothing extraordinary was happening at all. She went with Anna when Rosa was put to bed for her siesta, and stood looking out of the window at the street below.

Then, without thinking, she said, 'I have a lovely view from my balcony.'

She was startled when Rosa replied, 'I hate the sea—it's got sharks.'

Kate turned round. 'Has it? It looks so beautiful—I never thought of sharks.'

Rosa nodded. 'They eat you if you go in the water.'

Kate sat down on the edge of the bed. Anna had tucked the child up under a thin sheet, but Rosa had pushed it back. The room was stifling. If only there was an electric fan!

'Oh, Rosa, is it really full of sharks?' Kate said rather sadly. 'I was so looking forward to swimming.'

'Can you swim?' Rosa asked. 'Don't you just drown?'

Kate shook her head. 'Oh no, not when you've learnt how to do it. It's a wonderful feeling, floating. You lie on your back, looking at the sky, and you just rock slowly. It's like . . . like being rocked to sleep as a baby.'

Rosa didn't look impressed. 'I'd be afraid of being eaten,' she remarked.

Kate smiled at her. My poor baby, she thought, you're afraid of everything.

Later, they went for a walk—Rosa and Kate, with Anna, walking a few paces behind. It wasn't a very encouraging walk, Kate thought, for she was still afraid of thrusting friendship on Rosa. Then she remembered the advice she had been given once and asked Rosa the names in Portuguese of different objects. Rosa seemed to enjoy teaching a grown-up and even laughed if Kate made a mistake. It was always a very hesitant laugh, as if it had been shocked out of her, and Rosa looked surprised and a little worried about it herself.

That first night, too, was difficult. Kate stayed in the background as Anna bathed Rosa and put her to bed. Anna stood back when Kate went forward to tuck the child up. Kate hesitated. Dare she risk antagonising Anna so soon? But she could not resist the small quiet face of the child lying so meekly in bed—and she stooped swiftly, letting her mouth touch Rosa's forehead.

'Good night, pleasant dreams and God bless you, darling,' she said softly, and hurried from the room.

Her dinner was served in solitary state in the nursery. It was a relief to be alone, but she wondered with some amusement if the Senhora thought it a punishment.

That night Kate wrote a long letter home, telling her mother more about the job and its difficulties and ending up by saying she thought things were going to be much, much easier than she had feared. Then she re-read it, and hesitated; then she laughed at herself. She *had* mentioned Mr. Lister rather a lot in her letter, but then, after all, he was her employer, so that was natural. She had said what a strange man of moods he was—how friendly when she left him to go shopping and yet with a slightly cool suspicion when she rejoined him.

Then she thought of something and, her hand flew to her mouth in dismay. Had Mr. Lister gazed out of his office window and seen her crossing the street? Had he seen that wretched Portuguese man stop her? Perhaps he thought Kate had arranged to meet him? Her cheeks burned with dismay. Oh—no!

Antonio whatever-his-name-was had not struck her as a nice type—she was sure Mrs. McCormack would not approve of him—and perhaps Mr. Lister felt the same.

What could she do about it? Nothing at all, she realised unhappily.

Of course all the days were not like the first one, but as they passed, Kate began to feel she was progressing a little. Rosa no longer shrunk back when Kate entered the room, nor moved swiftly to Anna, to cling to her hand. Rosa even called Kate by her name—though not very often, and then in a timid voice as if expecting to be in trouble for having spoken to her. Kate felt that the daily walks were the most difficult—Anna's whole resentful attitude suggested to Kate that if she was not with them the walks would have been mere strolls to the street corner, where Anna could stand, chatting and giggling to the other girls or African house-boys, while Rosa stood patiently waiting.

Every time they went out Kate would see these little groups, and noticed the way Anna glanced wistfully towards them. Kate's heart ached for the small children left so casually to a servant's care, and wondered if their mothers knew what happened when their children went out for walks. But it made her hope that perhaps Anna would be glad to be relieved of her burden of escorting them, when the time came. Kate often thought they made a strange procession, she and Rosa walking in front, not touching, barely talking to one another, while Anna mooched along behind reluctantly.

Then one day Kate began to tell a story. It had to be simple because Rosa's English, while very good, considering she had grown up in a Portuguese-speaking family, was not as fluent as it should be.

Kate spoke as if talking to herself yet loudly enough for Rosa to hear. Then she would pause, and, if she waited long enough, Rosa might prompt her:

'And the little girl—she did cry?'

Kate, pretending not to notice the interruption, would continue the story, answering the question.

The day that, crossing the road, Rosa slipped her hand confidingly in to Kate's was a red-letter day. As later she told Mrs. McCormack: 'I really knew then that Rosa was beginning to trust me.'

One day, Kate ventured to say to Rosa, 'Poor Anna, how she hates walking.'

Rosa looked up with a smile. 'She likes to talk.'

They laughed together, sharing the joke.

'Poor Anna shall we let her go and talk?' Kate said hesitantly.

Rosa's eyes shone. 'She will be so happy,' she turned and told Anna. The African girl stared at them, said something in her own language which apparently Rosa understood,

96

showed flashing white teeth in a big smile—
and darted over the road to join one of the
groups of Africans talking on the corner.

Kate took a deep breath. *Anna would be so
happy?* Well, so was Kate!

It made all the difference to their walks.
Anna seemed to sense what to do and always
left the flat with them and then joined them
before they reached home, but it meant that
Kate no longer had the dark glowering face
behind her, or felt those resentful eyes boring
into her back. And, of course, she and Rosa
could talk more freely.

They grew more ambitious with their walks,
wandering along the sea front, going into the
parks, Kate's knowledge of Portuguese
progressing slowly but surely all the time as
she built up her friendship with the child.

Mrs. McCormack, whom Kate visited
frequently—too frequently, Kate said rather
apologetically once, and was immediately told
not to be so foolish, she could not go too
often—was thrilled with the progress Kate was
making.

'I should think Mr. Lister is very pleased,
isn't he?'

Kate had to admit that she had not seen him
since that first day. Mrs. McCormack stared at
her in amazement.

'Doesn't he ever visit his daughter?'

Kate flushed. She hated anyone to put the
wrong interpretation on her employer's

behaviour. 'Perhaps he thinks it's better to leave me to manage alone.'

Mrs. McCormack snorted. 'He's taking the easiest way out of it. How are they treating you now, dear? Better?'

Kate, looking round the pretty house appreciatively—she often slipped out in the evening after Rosa was safely asleep—smiled. 'Oh, yes, in their own odd way. Actually they ignore me. Sometimes I see Mariana and then she looks right through me. I don't mind. We have nothing in common.'

But Kate did mind, a little. No one likes being treated as non-existent, and in any case, she was aware that Mariana resented her existence and was merely trying to be unpleasant. She thought of Mariana's amused glances if she saw Kate with Rosa, trying to talk Portuguese—or when Kate went into a meal with the child, Anna carrying the tray with their food on it. Mariana's whole attitude was:

Kate is a servant, like Anna, so we don't need to talk to her.

It was silly to mind. But Kate still minded. She was young enough, too, to be hurt on the several occasions when the Dominguez had visitors, and laughter and high voices filled the flat. The Senhora always sent a note, requesting Kate to 'remain in her room as we wish to be alone.' Kate's cheeks burned as she read the first one and then crumpled it up. Did they think she wanted to force herself on them—that she was interested? But hearing the laughter and the music, it was hard not to feel out of things as she sat alone on her little balcony, gazing out to sea.

Another little habit of the Dominguez was that the Senhora would send for Rosa just as she was ready to go for her walk, and Kate must sit, waiting, in her room, knowing they were deliberately asserting their power by keeping the child. And then, the next moment, Kate would be ashamed of her unkind thought and tell herself that they loved Rosa, too, and were entitled to her company. But every time Rosa was with the Dominguez, she changed a little. Each visit made her retreat slightly from Kate, so that Kate wondered what they said to her.

One day, Mrs. McCormack asked Kate to take Rosa to tea. 'I would like to meet her, dear child,' she explained.

Kate hesitated. Mrs. McCormack looked, for once, annoyed. 'My dear child, this isn't a slum. How can they object?'

'I wonder if I should ask them,' Kate said, always very conscious of the need not to offend the Dominguez.

Mrs. McCormack snorted, 'If in doubt, don't.'

So Kate took Rosa to the Villa Paradis. This time she took Anna with them and Anna looked quite pleased to vanish with Mrs.

McCormack's housegirl. Kate felt this was more honest than taking Rosa on her own—at least, the Dominguez could not accuse her of doing it behind their backs!

Kate wondered a little how Rosa would react, but she might have known that Mrs. McCormack would make the child feel at home. Without hesitation she took Rosa on her knee and took her 'to Banbury Cross to see a fine lady ride on a white horse.' Rosa had, obviously, never heard the nursery rhyme before and her eyes shone like stars, although she remembered her good manners and said politely:

'*Mais—mais*—again, pleeze.'

Mrs. McCormack made herself breathless by singing all the nursery rhymes she could remember, and then she produced an enormous tin. 'I always give these to my child visitors,' she told Kate in an aside. 'I've been collecting them for years. Most children find them fascinating.'

So did Rosa, for the tin was full of buttons, of all sizes, shapes and colours. Rosa's face was absorbed as she arranged them in patterns.

Kate and Mrs. McCormack realised that the child had quite forgotten them.

'All she needs,' Mrs. McCormack said firmly, 'is love and laughter. Fancy, she had never heard a nursery rhyme before. It is so sad.'

'I never thought of them,' Kate confessed.

'They seem so young for her.'

'My dear child, you must realise that mentally Rosa is very young. She has had no babyhood at all. What a lot she has missed, poor wee thing. Start right from the beginning, Kate. It will help her English, too, make it less stilted. "This little pig went to market" is one all children adore . . .' She laughed at Kate's expression. 'Treat her as if she is a baby. She'll love it.'

How right Mrs. McCormack proved. Kate found as the days passed that the silly little games of babyhood brought her even closer to Rosa—who in turn taught them to Anna so that, in the end, all of them were dissolved into giggles. Oddly enough, Kate found that a different relationship was springing up between herself and the hitherto hostile African girl. Now Anna smiled at her and greeted her—even waited on her, if she noticed Kate needed anything. It certainly made the whole atmosphere easier to bear.

And then, just as Kate was feeling she could relax a little—that she had managed to avoid offending the Dominguez, that she was closer to Rosa than she had hoped to be in such a short time—her good luck changed.

Anna had gone to hospital with food poisoning, and the Senhora, in a very disagreeable voice, told Kate that Rosa should 'rest' instead of going out in the heat for these foolish expeditions. Kate, for once, stood up to the elderly woman. Anna might be away for some time and Kate felt that their daily walks must not be interfered with, because both she and Rosa needed them.

The Senhora's face was harsh. 'It is not done, in this country, for a young girl to make an expedition without a servant.'

'We won't get lost,' Kate said stubbornly.

The Senhora glared at her, shrugged her shoulders. 'I have warned you—'

Feeling rather sad about the little fracas, Kate set out. It was the first time she had stood up to the older woman, but somehow it had seemed to her important. It was also her first chance to take Rosa down town, and they set out on the bus, Rosa obviously enjoying the treat. Kate began to plan future outings. There was the cathedral to see—an aquarium, and Natala had said that Radio House welcomed visitors. If Rosa could meet more people and see interesting things that encouraged her to think, it would help her English, and also help her overcome the bouts of fear she occasionally suffered.

They went into the museum, and Kate loved it, especially as she explained things to Rosa and watched the small face light up intelligently. When they left, Kate was surprised to see how long they had been inside and they had to hurry to the bus stop.

It was an extremely hot day. The backs of their thin frocks were sticking to them, the small beads of water trickling down their faces. Kate pushed back her hair that suddenly felt heavy and looked down at the child. But Rosa, apart from naturally flushed cheeks, looked very well. Her small sticky hand clung to Kate's as they crossed the busy street, and they were talking animatedly when two tall men stopped in front of them on the pavement and spoke to them.

Kate stared at them. She could not understand a word of what they said—they spoke too fast, and her Portuguese was still very laboured. Politely she tried to explain, imagining they were lost, and asking her the way.

'*Falo um pouco o portuguese—*' she said stumblingly, trying to explain how very little she knew.

To her dismay, one man caught hold of her bare arm, his fingers clinging, and the other tried to push him out of the way, his bold eyes flashing.

Kate realised, with horror, that they were trying to 'pick her up.'

Rosa tugged at Kate's hand and there was fear on her face. Kate tried to free her arm and walk round the two men, but they were both talking excitedly, blocking the way. Kate's cheeks were on fire by now and she stared round anxiously. She did not want a scene in public, but how did one cope with such a situation?

And then came rescue.

But why had it to be Antonio Vidal, of all people?

He spoke curtly to the two men, who answered angrily and burst into what sounded like very rude laughter, then sauntered off, gazing over their shoulders. Antonio took Kate's arm. Kate removed it firmly and tried to smile.

'Thank you, Senhor Vidal,' she said very coldly. How unfortunate that he should have come along at that moment—and yet she should be grateful to him, for it had been an embarrassing situation, and she had really felt nervous.

She had seen Antonio Vidal several times when out for walks with Rosa, but had always managed to keep him at a distance, so far. Now she was under an obligation to him.

'Thank you,' she said, not quite so coldly, for he had accepted the way she removed her arm from his fingers and was looking, for him, quite humble. 'I am grateful for your assistance,' she went on formally. 'I'm afraid we must hurry, for we must catch the next bus.'

'I do not think you will be successful,' he told her, with that arrogant amused smirk that always irritated her. 'Look for yourself.'

As he spoke, the bus they were waiting for went past, the exhaust pipe belching black smoke—not that it would have stopped had she hailed it, for it was crowded. In dismay

Kate realised that this was the rush hour.

'We'll take a taxi,' she said to Rosa, hoping there would be one somewhere near. Unfortunately, in Mozambique, taxis did not cruise about the streets as they did in England, looking for fares. You had to find a taxi rank or else telephone a garage.

'My car is at your convenience, senhorita,' Antonio told her.

Kate hesitated, looking down at Rosa. Rosa's eyes were huge with fear—she obviously sensed Kate's uneasiness and shared it. She looked very tired. There seemed no choice, so, with as good a grace as she could muster, Kate followed Antonio to the long black sports car parked by the pavement. Rosa sat on her lap, and Kate's tiredness and fears vanished miraculously when Rosa, with the most natural gesture in the world, put her head against Kate's shoulder and fell asleep.

Antonio did not speak. He drove fast but expertly, weaving in and out of the traffic, and soon they were outside the Pensao Fadora.

Randel Lister's car was parked outside, and Kate's heart lifted with joy. It was so long since she had seen him.

Antonio helped her out of the car and she carried Rosa to the front door.

'Thank you very much . . .' she began, and the door opened abruptly.

Randel Lister stood there, Mariana by his side. He almost snatched Rosa out of Kate's arms, his face furious. 'Is she hurt?'

Kate was startled, not only by the question but by the anger he showed. 'No, only tired. We found the buses were full, and . . .'

Mariana came closer, looking slim and glamorous in a sheath frock of tangerine silk, her hair coiled loosely, her dark eyes bright. 'My poor *bébé*—the sun-madness. My mother has been anguished. Why are you so late?'

Then she saw Antonio. He had stood aside, a small enigmatic smile curving his mouth.

'So!' Mariana went on, her voice rising in anger. 'This is what you do. Do you not know that you are employed to look after the *bébé* and not to make the rendezvous with Senhor Vidal?'

Kate gasped and just found her voice, but Antonio spoke first.

'I am desolated—' he said, spreading out his hands expressively, 'but it was not a rendezvous. Alas, it was most unromantic. The Senhorita was waiting for a bus—' he pronounced it *boos*—'and I was happy to offer them a lift home.'

Randel was holding his daughter in his arms, gazing down worriedly at the little face. Now he looked at Kate, his eyes cold. She caught her breath. He did not believe it.

'It's true,' she said. Turning her head, she saw the amusement in Antonio's eyes and caught her breath again with more dismay. She had unconsciously linked herself with him in a

106

CHAPTER VII

That night was a nightmare to Kate. As she told Mrs. McCormack the following day, sitting on a pouffe, her hands clasped round her knees, her young face desolate and tired, she had awakened some time in the night to hear the sound of frightened sobbing.

'Naturally I went to see if it was Rosa,' Kate said unhappily, looking up at her friend. 'It was—it was too awful for words.' Her voice began to shake and she had to bite into her lower lip for a moment before she could continue. 'Rosa saw me and began to scream . . .'

She shuddered, burying her face in her hands for a moment.

'And then?' Mrs. McCormack said softly.

Kate looked up. 'Everything got worse and worse. Mariana was there then the Senhora, and there was a terrible scene, with Rosa screaming and screaming and no one able to stop her. I tried to, but Mariana pushed me aside. She said it was all my fault, that I had overtired the child. That I was *incompetenta*—and the Senhora told me to go to my room and . . .' Kate paused. 'In the end the Senhora gave Rosa some pills and she fell asleep.'

Mrs. McCormack was looking puzzled. 'I don't see why Rosa should have had a nightmare like that, Kate. It was not so very alarming, was it, your little encounter with those two men?'

Kate sighed. 'I don't know how a child reacts. I'm afraid I did panic a little. I didn't know how to get rid of them and I was so afraid there might be a scene in the street. She may have sensed my fear. Then—then I don't like Antonio Vidal and . . . and I think Rosa knows that, too. But . . . she did go to sleep in my arms in the car—'

'Exactly,' Mrs. McCormack said triumphantly, as if she had driven some point home. 'That's what I'm getting at, Kate. If she had been so afraid then, she would not have relaxed in the car. Did she wake up when you put her to bed?'

'Only a little . . . She was very sleepy, but she said it had been *the good fun.*' Kate's voice faltered as she repeated Rosa's favourite English expression.

Mrs. McCormack nodded. 'Then something else worried her. Did . . . did the Dominguez go near her after she was in bed?'

Kate tried to remember. 'They were all out. I think—think Mr. Lister took them out—' Her young face was suddenly desolate, showing the hurt disappointment at his behaviour. 'But . . . but I was reading in bed when they returned. At least, when Mariana and her mother returned. I heard them talking, and a door open, but I put out my light

109

at once, and I was so tired, I fell asleep. I don't know if they went in to Rosa.' She realised suddenly that Mrs. McCormack must have a reason for her questions. 'Why?'

Mrs. McCormack smiled. 'I just wondered. You see, Kate, I think that when Rosa has these bouts of fear, they are because of seeds of distrust dropped deliberately in her mind.'

'Oh no,' Kate said quickly. 'Surely no one could be so cruel!'

Mrs. McCormack smiled enigmatically. 'My dear, you have no idea how cruel people can be and cloak it by calling it something else. What happened this morning?'

Kate told her about the humiliation of apologising to the Senhora, of her obvious triumph, her unpleasant remarks about young women who thought they knew better than their elders. 'And they kept Rosa in bed all this morning. This afternoon, Mariana has taken her out somewhere. I haven't seen her all day.' Kate sighed again. She looked at her watch. 'I think I should go back now. I may have the chance to put her to bed.'

Mrs. McCormack went with her to the door. 'Bring her to tea again, as soon as you can, Kate dear. Oh yes—' she looked happy as she remembered something—'James wants to know when you are coming to dinner. He wants to see you again.'

'I'd love to, some time, but just at the moment . . .'

Mrs. McCormack's smile was sympathetic. 'I know, dear child, you have to *walkee very carefullee—*'

Kate left her, feeling better for the little talk, and wondering if Mrs. McCormack could be right and if the Dominguez *were* still deliberately planting seeds of fear in Rosa's mind. If so, how could they be fought?

Natala was at the desk in the hall and greeted Kate with a warm smile.

'Oh, Natala,' Kate said from the depths of her unhappiness. 'I feel I'm fighting something too strong for me. I don't know what to do.'

Natala asked what was wrong, and into her sympathetic ears Kate poured the whole story again. Natala seemed to understand.

'But, of course, Mariana is jealous because Antonio likes you. He is very handsome—that one.'

'Antonio—likes me?' Kate said, amazed. 'I don't think so. I'm just another girl to be slain by his charm,' she added bitterly. 'He's too bold.'

Natala looked horrified. 'But you must understand that it is—natural for him to look at you—how you say it?—*boldly.* You are an Englese girl—that is what makes it right. The girls of good family here are sheltered, and it is usual for their marriages to be arranged. They do not meet young men on the streets or walk about . . .' She stopped, and paged quickly through a dictionary she always kept on the

111

shelf underneath the desk. 'Unchaperoned.' She said the long word with some difficulty and much pride.

'I see—we are fair game,' Kate said bitterly. 'They can insult us as much as they like.'

'Oh, no!' Natala was nearly in tears. She caught Kate's hand. 'It is not that way—not at all—*Kett.* I do not make myself the clear way. I have given you the offence.'

Kate patted her hand. 'Of course you haven't, Natala. I must be dumb—I misunderstood you. Go on.'

Natala smiled gratefully. 'I do not think that Antonio means to be *bold*—it is just that, with you, he can feel at ease. Perhaps he offends because he does not know how much at ease he may be with an Englese girl.'

Kate had to smile. 'Yes, I see what you mean. It must be difficult for him.' Kate allowed. 'After all, he did rescue me from an embarrassing situation, and he might have made trouble with Mr. Lister and he didn't. Perhaps I have misjudged him.'

Natala said quickly, 'Antonio can be very kind.' Kate looked at her and saw that the girl's mouth was trembling. 'Ah,' Natala said. 'You have guessed my secret.'

'Oh, Natala—and he likes you?' Kate's voice was sympathetic.

To her dismay, the other girl's eyes filled with tears. 'Ah, no—to him, I am an embarrassment. It is Mariana he loves—

though he finds you extremely—extremely—'
She was searching for a word, and then found
it—'enchanting.'

Kate felt her cheeks burn. 'And Mariana?'

Natala shrugged. 'Antonio is a man. To
Mariana, all men are prey.' Her voice was
bitter. 'Their eyes must not stray. That is why
she hates you. First Mr. Leester, he engage
you to care for his *bébé*—then Antonio, he like
you too much. So she will hurt you if she can.'

Kate was feeling embarrassed at the way the
conversation was going, so she changed the
subject by asking questions about the Pensio.
She could not understand why the Dominguez
lived there and not in a house. Natala told her
that, as a rule, Mariana was away, often in
foreign countries. That the Senhora could not
keep a servant—that Anna only stayed
because of devotion for the *bébé*.

Kate looked at her watch and saw that it
was late. Natala told her that Mariana had not
brought Rosa home yet.

'She is out with Mr. Lister, I believe,' Natala
went on, and Kate tried not to wonder what
fresh lies Mariana was inventing. As they
parted, Natala said shyly, 'I do not understand
you, *Kett*. If Antonio looked at me with his
eyes as he looks at you, I would be so happy—'
With a funny little poignant gesture, she laid
her hand on her heart.

Kate looked at her affectionately. 'Dear
Natala! I wish—'

She sighed as she mounted the steps to the dreary inhospitable flat. Poor Natala—she deserved someone who would be kind to her. There were so few men . . .

On her balcony, with the door ajar, wondering if she would be allowed to see Rosa that day, Kate wrote home again, carefully leaving out the account of her trip to the museum and its unfortunate outcome. She felt that she had slipped back in her relationship with Rosa and that all her work was wasted.

Next day she went to see her employer and said as much.

He had told her rather curtly that he was busy, but when she insisted, he agreed to see her for half an hour. He sat staring at her, his lean face cold and sceptical, she felt, as she explained unhappily about the afternoon. During the long sleepless night, when the tears burned her eyelids because Mariana had put Rosa to bed and refused to allow Kate into the room, 'The *bébé* will only scream again and she will be ill,' Mariana had said curtly—Kate had decided to tell Mr. Lister the whole story.

Now she found it hard to talk to him, facing his cold eyes, wondering how to fight the confidence he had in Mariana.

'I thought it would help her English if we went over the museum—she teaches me the Portuguese words, too, so it is a sort of mutual-help partnership,' Kate said, staring at the desk, the telephone, the window, anything rather than let her eyes meet his. Even now, in her distress, she was conscious of the breathlessness she always felt when he was near. She felt alive—vibrant with youth and the joy of living. It was a strange feeling. When she was with Mr. Lister, life became exciting, she wondered what was waiting round the corner. Dismissal, she thought wryly, as she had thought once before.

'Rosa loved it, Mr. Lister,' Kate explained; she looked up, met his eyes and saw that he was no longer quite so coldly incredulous but that she had caught his interest. It took a few seconds for her to compose herself and find the right words. 'She is very intelligent. Until now, she had just—just lived, eaten, slept, walked to street corners where Anna talked . . .' Kate could not resist saying, though it sounded rather malicious, 'We had so much fun there that I had no idea it was so late, and then . . .then . . .' She paused and swallowed. She looked at Mr. Lister and saw that he was frowning.

'Then you met Vidal,' he said coldly. 'I know he defended you, but I understand it *was* by appointment.'

Kate's face felt as if it had been slapped. 'But that's a lie,' she said indignantly. 'Why, I can't stand the man.' Anger forced the truth out of her.

Mr. Lister was frowning. 'But I understand . . .'

Kate sat bolt upright, bristling with fury. 'I don't care what you *understand,*' she said with a rudeness that startled her, 'but I'm telling the truth. I met him when I first went to the Pensao Fadora, and several times he's stopped me in the street and asked me to have coffee with him. I have always refused, for I don't like him.'

'I see,' Mr. Lister said quietly. Kate looked up. She had expected him to rebuke her for her rudeness, but instead he was gazing at her thoughtfully. 'So?'

She started again, clenching her hands, trying to be calm. Her little burst of anger had shaken her. It must be Mariana making Mr. Lister think that she was meeting Antonio. 'We . . . Rosa and I were hurrying to the bus stop and two—two men stopped me.' She felt her cheeks hot under Mr. Lister's quizzical gaze. 'I thought they were asking me the way. I tried to speak in Portuguese—I didn't realise . . .'

'Rather naïve of you,' Mr. Lister said in a dry voice.

Her face felt even hotter. 'I suppose it was, rather—' she admitted, humbly. 'I . . . I never think of things like that. It was rather embarrassing—and then Mr. Vidal turned up and—and got rid of them. I told him we were getting the bus, but I hadn't realised it was the rush hour, and when Mr. Vidal offered us a lift, I saw that Rosa was very tired and . . . and

116

accepted it.'

'I see.'

Mr. Lister spoke in such a strange voice that Kate dared to look at him again. He was doodling on his blotter with a pen, his face thoughtful.

'I see . . .' he said again, slowly. He looked up. 'I understand Rosa had a nightmare that evening.' He paused.

'Yes,' Kate admitted unhappily. She told him about the whole terrible episode. 'Of course, now the Dominguez blame me,' she finished sadly. 'They won't let me near Rosa.'

'What?' Mr. Lister's voice was sharp. 'But I understood—' He paused.

There was silence as they stared at one another. He began to drum his fingers on the table. Then he began to speak very slowly, as though thinking aloud. 'It is a difficult situation—for us all. I can see now that I should have thought it all out more carefully. You know, Kate, I realise it isn't always easy for you, but the—the Dominguez tell me you are very *difficult*—' He looked at her startled face and his voice softened. 'The Senhora is old and set in her ways—she doesn't understand youth. Mariana has looked after Rose as if the child was her own. I don't want to hurt them more than I can help.'

Surprisingly the rebellious, angry words bubbled out of Kate. She could no more control them than King Canute could stop the

117

tide. She looked Mr. Lister straight in the eyes as she spoke.

'I think you're forgetting Rosa. She is the one who is being hurt. I think it would be better to let me go back to England. Rosa is like a bone, being tugged at by fighting dogs. Rosa is the one we must think of—not you, or me, or—or the Dominguez—' She could not force herself to say Mariana's name. She stood up. 'We've been over this before, I know, but I do think you should seriously think of it, Mr. Lister. It's so bad for the poor child . . . I mean . . . it's so upsetting for her . . .' Her voice trembled. 'Rosa needs serenity, love, a secure, happy atmosphere. Not—not this emotional tug-of-war.'

Mr. Lister came round the desk to her side. He looked down at the young unhappy face lifted to his, saw the stark misery in the eyes, and he put gentle hands on her shoulders. She trembled under his touch and could only hope that he thought it was because she was upset.

'Kate,' he said gently. 'We can't do that. We'll find a way. Go back now and you will see that everything is going to be all right. I will telephone the Dominguez, and Rosa will be in your charge.'

'But she is afraid of me again,' Kate said a little wildly, 'And I can't bear it.'

'I don't think she is. Yesterday she talked to me about you—' Kate looked at him with quick interest and he nodded. 'She said you were speaking *the Portuguese with great fun—*' His voice as he copied Rosa's manner of speaking made them both laugh. He gave Kate's shoulders a reassuring squeeze and went on, 'I have to fly down to Johannesburg for a week, and when I come back you can report progress. If it doesn't work out as we want it to, we'll make a plan, see?' He smiled down at her, and Kate felt as if her heart had flipped over. She could only smile back. Did he mean by 'a plan,' perhaps, that he would take a villa and let them live with him? That would be a perfect solution, all their troubles solved. 'So, Kate, stick it out for a week, will you?'

She agreed and left him, comforted by his words—feeling that now he understood, things would be easier.

CHAPTER VIII

To Kate, the week when Randel Lister was away dragged—yet, all the same, it had its good moments. Sometimes she felt she had to start all over again with Rosa, for although Mr. Lister had obviously talked plainly to the Dominguez and the original pattern of Kate's life with Rosa was once more restored, it seemed to Kate that the child watched her all the time nervously. On the other hand,

Mariana was away. Kate wondered if Mariana had gone to Johannesburg with Randel Lister, but Natala, who seemed to know everything, said that she had gone to stay with a friend in Mauritius.

'A wealthy French familee,' Natala said, her eyes bright. 'They are sugar people.' She shook her head. 'That is Mariana's—how you say it?—cup of soup?'

Trying not to chuckle, for Natala was sensitive, Kate corrected her, 'Cup of tea, Natala.'

'Thank you. This man, he is very handsome but shrewd.' Natala whistled softly. 'So shrewd that I do not think Mariana could pull a loose one on him.'

Kate, trying to stifle her chuckles, wondered where on earth Natala learned her English idioms. She knew Natala read assiduously everything in English she could lay her hands on—magazines, library books, newspapers.

'Is she in love with him? I thought . . .' Kate began, and stopped. She would never discuss Mr. Lister with Natala—nor what Mr. Lister thought of Mariana.

Natala looked at her. 'You are mad, you know that, *Kett*? Mariana loves only— Mariana.'

Kate hoped Mariana would still be away when Mr. Lister came back, but she was not. The first thing Kate knew of his return was when he telephoned her. His voice was pleasantly concerned.

'How goes it, Kate?'

It was difficult to be honest when she knew everyone could hear what she said.

'Not too badly,' she said cautiously.

He chuckled. It was a warm friendly chuckle. Kate noticed with a strange dispassionate vision that she felt just as thrilled when she heard his voice on the phone as when he was in the room with her.

He told her that he was planning a party at the Polana and that she was invited. He wondered who she would like to ask as her partner—'I thought of Antonio for you,' he finished.

She felt cold all over. 'Oh, no—please!' she said quickly. Whatever had made him think of Antonio Vidal, when she had expressly told Mr. Lister how much she disliked that young Portuguese? Then she knew—Mariana. She took a deep breath. 'Mr. Lister, if it's all the same to you, I would like to ask James McCormack.'

'James McCormack? I seem to know the name. How did you meet him?' Mr. Lister enquired, and there was a strange note in his voice.

For one rebellious moment Kate was tempted to ask him if it was his business. Then she thought again and realised that maybe it was. 'I came out on the ship with his mother. I visit them frequently—they are my best friends here.'

There was a pause. Mr. Lister sounded guilty. 'Your only friends, I'm afraid.'

'Oh, no,' Kate said quickly. Mrs. McCormack had bitterly criticised Randel Lister once for not introducing Kate to the English circle in Lourenço Marques. She had said it looked odd—that it gave Mrs. Kelly a chance to gossip about it. 'Oh, no—I have Natala. She works here.'

'Oh, yes, Mariana was talking about her the other day. She said she was impudent. She's deformed, isn't she?'

Kate's cheeks were flagged with anger. 'She is *not* deformed—she is a spastic. She should go to hospital, but she has no money—she has to support a sick mother.'

'I see.' He did not sound very interested. 'I suppose that's why she's so bad-tempered.'

Kate's temper flared again. 'She is not bad-tempered,' she began, and then gave it up. If Mariana had said Natala was bad-tempered, then Randel Lister would believe her. Why bother to try to make him believe the truth?

The dance was a great success. James accepted her invitation, and it was a hot, beautiful evening when they all went to the enormous, luxurious white hotel. Kate had bought a new dress. It was of chiffon, palest blue, expensive, but worth every penny. James had sent her two orchids, which she pinned to her shoulder. Then she saw Mariana and wondered why she had wasted money on the frock. Who would look at her when Mariana stood there—very beautiful, very sophisticated, in a sheath-like frock, very severe and plain, showing up every line of her beautiful body? Her only ornaments were two enormous pearl earrings and two camellias tucked into the black chignon that lay low on her neck—Every movement Mariana made was deliberately planned to be provocative. Kate stared at the warm olive skin and the dark red, full mouth, those deep liquid eyes in which a man could surely drown . . .

Kate turned away, sighing a little, and saw James's eyes twinkling at her.

He took her in his arms and they circled the floor slowly. 'I think you're much prettier,' he whispered.

'Oh, James, thank you,' Kate whispered back. 'You're always so kind.'

'I mean it,' he said. There was a note of sincerity in his voice that startled her. She looked up into his blue eyes and saw the affectionate kindness there that she always saw in his mother's face. 'I like you very much indeed, Kate,' he said, his arm tightening round her. 'I find Mariana a bit too obvious.'

Randel certainly didn't, Kate thought as the evening began. He hardly left Mariana's side, gazing into her eyes, looking absolutely bewitched. Not that Kate could blame him. All the men revolved round Mariana, like moths round a candle.

It was a new Mariana Kate was seeing—a gay, laughing, amusing girl, flinging back her head, showing a long beautiful neck, turning with a magical magnetism from one adoring face to another.

Kate had no idea how much of this she showed on her face as she sat watching Mariana—and she was quite surprised when Randel Lister asked her to dance.

She felt so nervous that at first it was agony. Her feet seemed to have grown several sizes too long and she could do nothing right. Randel smiled down at her and said teasingly, 'Relax, Kate, I'm not going to eat you.'

She looked up at him, her eyes eloquent. 'It's not that. It's just . . .' As it so often did, the truth came bubbling out because she was unprepared. 'Just that it must be awful dancing with me after Mariana.'

He looked surprised. 'That's nonsense. Actually you dance much better than Mariana. She clings and is quite heavy.'

Kate stared at him, her eyes glowing. 'Oh, thank you,' she said. She could not believe it. She danced better than Mariana!

Randel was laughing. 'So relax and let's enjoy this.'

She obeyed, and it was wonderful. She thought of *My Fair Lady* and for the first time understood and appreciated the poignancy of the lovely tune, *I Could Have Danced All Night.*

She felt just like that, and she was only sorry when it ended and they went back to the table.

Mariana was talking quietly and earnestly to James, her face intent. She looked up as Randel and Kate joined them, and then resumed her conversation. Randel offered Kate a cigarette and they began to talk idly. He was clever at encouraging shy people, and Kate soon found herself telling him some of the many interesting Portuguese customs about which Natala had told her. Kate was surprised to find how little Randel knew about the country or the people, and he confessed with very disarming humility that he was afraid he had always put his work first.

'It's a pity,' Kate said slowly, 'for you miss so much.'

She failed to notice his quick surprised look, or to realise that Randel was seeing Kate as a woman—and a surprisingly attractive woman —for the first time.

Then they talked about Rosa, but it was difficult, for Kate could not be honest. All sorts of angry words boiled inside her, but she felt she could not berate a man who was entertaining her for the evening. Besides, she knew that it was not entirely his fault. He loved and trusted Mariana—so how could he be expected to see the kind of tricks she could be up to, the despicable things she would do to an innocent, helpless child?

She danced several times with Randel and

was surprised that Mariana permitted it. But Mariana, at the moment, seemed only interested in James.

Once, walking back to their table, Mr. Lister said a strange thing.

'Mariana doesn't realise how she is monopolising your partner. Do you mind, Kate?'

Kate lifted startled, honest eyes. 'Mind? Of course not. If he *was* mine, he wouldn't want to wander, so I would trust him. As he isn't mine, he can do what he likes. In any case, I wouldn't worry. Mariana isn't really interested. It's only because he is another man and she collects scalps like a Red Indian would, just for the fun of the chase.' Kate spoke unthinkingly, and then realised what she had said.

There was an appalled hush. Both she and Randel instinctively stood still as they stared at one another. Then Randel recovered. He gave a wry laugh.

'You've hit the nail right on the head. That's exactly what Mariana does.'

He sounded almost proud of her, Kate thought unhappily. But, thanks be, he was not offended by Kate's frankness.

The band struck up again. Randel looked at the table. Mariana was touching James's hand with her long fingers, gently, tantalisingly. Randel looked down at the quiet, pleasant girl by his side. 'My favourite tune,' he said. 'Shall we dance?'

lie. Grateful as she was because Antonio had not mentioned the embarrassing encounter, for she was sure Mr. Lister would have disapproved, now she felt under an obligation to Antonio.

Randel was thanking Antonio stiffly. Turning to Kate, he said, 'I will carry Rose upstairs, and she must go to bed. In future, kindly see that she is home at the right time. I also think the Senhora deserves an apology for the anxiety your thoughtlessness has caused her.'

Outwardly meek, Kate followed him up to the flat, seething with the injustice of it, yet admitting honestly to herself that it had looked bad, coming home with such a man as Antonio. No doubt the Dominguez had done all they could to make matters worse. How delighted the Senhora would be when Kate apologised! That would be a bitter pill to swallow, but somehow it had to be done.

She quickly put the sleepy Rosa to bed, but when she went out of the bedroom the flat was quiet. Mariana, her mother and Randel must have gone out. Kate went to her own room and had a bath, hoping the unfortunate afternoon would not have disastrous after-effects.

Kate looked at him, and although she did not know it, all her heart was in her eyes. 'Oh, please,' she said softly.

But everything has to end, and finally it was time to go home. James drove Kate, teasing her as he drove her back to the Pensio. 'Wasn't I a good boy?' he demanded. 'I lured the tigress away to give you a chance to bewitch the ogre. Did you succeed?'

'Oh, James,' Kate said disconsolately. 'He dances wonderfully, but I was only a substitute for Mariana. What girl can be happy to be that?'

'I'm not so sure,' James said cheerfully. 'He looked as if he was enjoying himself.'

'Did he?' Kate ventured to hope for a moment, but common sense prevailed. 'I think he feels a bit guilty about me, so wanted to give me a good time,'

James grunted and stopped the car outside the dingy building.

'You're too modest, that's your trouble.'

That was something his mother was always telling her. And she repeated it a few days later when Kate had taken Rosa round to the Villa Paradis to tea.

'James says you need more self-confidence, and I agree, dear child,' observed Mrs. McCormack.

Kate had a headache, and Mrs. McCormack made her take aspirin, put an eau de cologne-soaked hankie on her forehead and made her lie down. Then she took Rosa on her knee and told her about the days when James was a small boy.

Rosa looked relaxed, leaning against Mrs. McCormack's ample bosom and looking confidingly up into the kind face, as Mrs. McCormack told Kate later.

'. . . And we walked down Regent Street. That's in London, you know, Rosa,' Mrs. McCormack said, and then saw the child had gone very white and felt her shiver.

'In London people die,' Rosa said. She shuddered, her small body trembling. Mrs. McCormack tightened her arms, but before she could speak, Rosa went on, 'Their heads are cut off.' Rosa bent her head and made an expressive movement with her hand across the back of her neck. Her eyes were wide and terrified.

When Mrs. McCormack had checked her first quick denial, she said gently, 'That's only in history, darling. They did that hundreds of years ago, but not any more. I've lived in London—so has James. So has Kate. We've all got our heads on,' she said.

Rosa's eyes were still huge. Suddenly she clutched Mrs. McCormack round the neck and whispered in her ear, 'Kate will take me to London and cut off my head.'

Later, when telling Kate about it, Mrs. McCormack said that her blood had run cold. 'I wanted to ask her who had said such wicked things, yet I was afraid it would frighten her more. So I told her that her father would never let anyone do that to her, and in any case, that Kate loved her so much that she would never let *anyone* hurt her. She asked me why you loved her, Kate. I said it was because you had always wanted a little girl of your own. "Like me?" Rosa asked, and when I said, "Yes, just like you," that seemed to make her happy. She cuddled up against me and told me that she had not thought you would hurt her, but *they* said so.' Mrs. McCormack sighed. 'We can guess who *they* are.'

Kate sighed. 'I just can't believe the Dominguez can be so wicked. My poor Rosa . . . no wonder she screamed when she saw me.'

'Has she been better since that afternoon?' Mrs. McCormack asked. They had met a few days after the event—the first time when an occasion for confidences could arise.

Kate nodded. 'Yes, I wondered why.' She gave the older woman a loving smile. 'I don't know what I'd do without you. You solve all my problems.'

'Not all,' Mrs. McCormack said slowly, and Kate could feel the slow betraying colour fill her checks. 'Not quite all, but I do my best,' Mrs. McCormack finished, smiling sympathetically.

With Rosa's new-found confidence in her, Kate decided on drastic measures. She and

Mrs. McCormack discussed it and then enlisted Natala's willing aid.

The first time Kate took Rosa through the back of the *Pensio* and to the small room Natala had arranged for her, Kate watched the child's face as she showed her the clothes she had bought her.

'For me?' Rosa's eyes sparkled. She touched the crisp gingham frock and the open-toed sandals with loving fingers. 'But . . .' her eyes were frightened.

Feeling rather guilty, Kate made a game of it. 'Daddy wants you to be an English girl, and these are English clothes—but your granny might be hurt if she saw you in them, so let's keep it a secret.'

Rosa adored that. Like all children she loved doing something to outwit the adult world; to be in league with another adult made it especially thrilling.

Who would have known this child? Kate thought, as they slipped out of the back entrance to the *Pensio.* An English girl in a pink gingham frock, her hair brushed like a cloud of spun glory, bare white knees, tiny white socks and sandals.

Rosa lifted a radiant face. 'I feel so light!' she exclaimed.

Of course she did, poor poppet, as Mrs. McCormack said when they went there to tea. Think of all those starched petticoats!

Gradually Kate made more changes. The

130

first time she took Rosa on the beach, Rosa could not believe it was true. She kept scooping handfuls of sand and letting it trickle through her fingers. As she went for her first paddle, she clung tightly to Kate's hand and giggled as the water tickled her toes. They built sand castles together, collecting shells and pebbles to decorate them.

It was sheer bliss to watch the change in Rosa. Sometimes Kate thought that the Dominguez and Randel Lister must be blind not to see how she had altered. Maybe they never looked at the child. Sometimes Kate's anger with Randel for his complete indifference to Rosa was so overwhelming that it was all she could do not to rush down to his office and tell him so.

Rosa did not *know* her father. If she spoke of him it was with awe. He was very busy, she explained, didn't like children talking, hated them to climb over him—all things she had obviously been told by Mariana.

Mariana! These days she was always out, so fortunately she had little chance to see Rosa. Both Mariana and the Senhora left Rosa entirely alone now, perhaps hoping to make Kate tired of the child. Kate never had time off, for Anna was still in hospital and had not been replaced. Not that Kate minded. She loved every moment she spent with Rosa.

Mrs. McCormack and James both remarked on the difference.

131

'She is a different child,' James said slowly, taking Rosa on his knee. He had come swimming with them and was going to teach Rosa to do a 'dog's paddle' to start with, winning her confidence.

When they came back from their swim in the small pool, Kate was half asleep. She opened her eyes and saw James's face blurring in the sunshine.

'Lazy!' he teased. He turned to Rosa. 'Let's cover her with sand and make her into a castle.'

Laughing, they were shovelling sand over her with their hands, when two shadows fell on them. Kate felt a chill suddenly and something made her open her eyes.

She found herself gazing up into Randel Lister's startled face and Mariana's hostile one.

'Oh!' she said guiltily, and tried to sit up.

'Hullo,' James said cheerfully. 'Come to join us?'

Randel was staring at his daughter. Kate could not interpret the strange look on his face. She wondered if he was wishing his wife, Candida, could have seen their 'little English rose' now. Rosa was wearing a minute green swimsuit, a floppy hat, covered with bright red poppies, on her head. Her bare legs were brown and she was chuckling as she scooped sand over Kate. Then Rosa turned her head and saw her father—and Kate's heart seemed to turn over with grief as she saw the fright and shock there, and she wondered how Randel felt when Rosa dived for James and he caught her, lifting her up in his arms to sit on his shoulders.

James was smiling as he looked at Randel Lister and Mariana. The angry words that burst from Mariana had obviously been held back only because she had expected Randel to speak to them.

'You see, Randel, I was right. She has an assignation on the sands. Is that the way to care for your *bébé?* And our poor Rosa . . .' Mariana went towards James, and Rosa promptly stuck her face in James's neck. 'Our poor Rosa,' Mariana went on, her voice changing. 'She is let run naked in front of all—she will get the sun-madness, and—'

Randel turned and looked at her. He said very quietly, 'Sometimes, Mariana, you talk the most absolute nonsense. In England, all our children play like this. We believe it is the right way to live. No, I suggest you go home. The beach has always bored you, as you have so often said. I'll telephone later tonight.'

He turned back and looked down at Kate, then at James, who was watching him with open amusement. 'Are you really teaching Rosa to swim?' Randel asked, his voice friendly.

James took the hint. 'We're just due for another lesson, aren't we, my poppet?' He put

133

the child on the ground, but she clung to his hand, still looking worriedly at her father.

Kate watched Mariana walking across the sands, twisting her high heels, stumbling, fury in every movement as she went. Then she watched James and Rosa walk down towards the sea together, hand in hand. Finally she turned and looked up at her employer. He had come to sit by her side and was staring at her strangely. She felt greatly handicapped, forced as she was still to lie on the ground. You could not be very dignified when you were halfway towards being made into a sand castle!

'Well?' Mr. Lister said, and she shivered at the cold note in his voice. 'I think you owe me an explanation, don't you?'

She moistened her lips nervously. 'I don't think I understand.'

He was watching James and the child, and there was the oddest look on his face. Kate thought for one wild moment that he looked almost envious.

'James is good with children,' he observed.

'Oh, he is,' Kate said quickly. 'But then James is wonderful with everyone. He is so kind.'

Mr. Lister looked at her frowning a little. 'Why the deception, Kate?' he asked, almost reproachfully. 'That was what upset Mariana.'

Kate stared at him. How blind could a man be?

'Do you think,' she said slowly, 'that had I

asked the Senhora's permission to take Rosa bathing, she would have granted it? She would have been hurt to know that when we are alone Rosa wears these clothes.' Kate stretched out and picked up the pink gingham frock and the sandals and showed them to Mr. Lister. 'These are English clothes, but the Senhora cannot be expected to realise that. I didn't want to offend her, so we did these things . . . on the sly, I suppose you might say,' she finished nervously.

He was scooping handfuls of sand and letting it trickle through his fingers. 'You think I've behaved very badly towards my daughter, don't you?'

The accusation, especially made in such a quiet voice, startled Kate.

'I . . .' She stopped as she met his eyes. She could feel the blood rushing guiltily to her face. 'I don't blame you,' she said cautiously. 'I think it's hard for a man to understand a little girl's needs. You see, really, Rosa shouldn't live in that dark flat and eat those highly seasoned foods. We rarely get fruit or vegetables. She needs much plainer food. The Pensio is ideal for the Senhora—she has no domestic troubles, can invite friends for bridge or parties—but it isn't really right for a little girl.' Her voice died away.

He was not looking at her. He was still trickling sand through his fingers. Then he looked across the sands towards where James

135

and Rosa were in the water.

To Kate's utter amazement, Randel began to tell her about the Dominguez, and how he had never met them until after his wife died.

'Candida worked in London as an interpreter. She was so—so gentle. We were married a month after we met—a year later, Rose was born. It coincided with a trip I had to make here. Candida was happy—she thought it romantic that Rose should be born here, where she herself was born. Then she died . . .' There was a silence, and as Kate watched his face, she longed to touch him gently, to comfort him. She could hardly bear to keep still, to wait for him to continue. 'I was nearly out of my mind,' he said simply. 'Then there was the baby. It was then that the Senhora Dominguez came to the nursing home. She brought Mariana . . . they were both hysterical with grief. They had been away—had just returned and heard the news.' He looked up as Kate made a little sound.

She stared at him but did not speak. The Senhora had told her a very different story, of hours spent by Candida's side as she died, how Candida had handed the small baby to her to 'love and care for'.

'They did not see . . . see your wife before?' Kate began softly.

Randel shook his head. 'I think she had quarrelled with her family. The Portuguese do not approve of their daughters roaming the

136

world. Candida allowed me to believe that she was an orphan, so you can imagine what a surprise it was for me when they turned up. And what a scene! Mariana adores scenes, as you know.' He smiled at her—a youthful *let's share a joke* smile. Kate was glad for his sake that he could smile. She wanted to cry. How he must have adored his wife. Lucky, lucky Candida!

Suddenly he startled her by saying, 'Do you think Rosa is normal for her age?'

Kate stared at him. Was this some more wickedness of Mariana's?

'Of course she is,' she said stoutly. 'It's just that the sort of experiences English children of her age have had she has never known. Do you realise that she had never heard of Cinderella, or the little pig that went to market? Nor been to a zoo, nor seen a clown? Never seen an elephant—or seen wild flowers growing—or had a pet of her own.' She stopped breathlessly.

Randel Lister was staring at her strangely. 'And you think these things are important?'

Kate began to brush off the sand. 'I don't think they're *important*,' she said, cross with his blindness and annoyed with herself for feeling so. After all, he was only a father—how could he be expected to know? 'I think they're essential.'

CHAPTER IX

It was later that evening that Kate stood on her balcony, gazing at the wonderful view and thinking with youthful glee that Mariana's spiteful attempt to cause trouble with Mr. Lister had completely misfired. Instead, it had the reverse effect. Talking on the beach while James and Rosa played in the shallow water, Kate had seen a different Randel Lister, a bewildered man, a man who wanted to do the right thing yet did not know what that was. Then when James had come up to the beach, being chased by Rosa, it had seemed natural for him to ask Randel back to his house for tea.

'Mother is longing to meet you,' James said with that friendly, sweet smile of his. 'Of course she adores Rosa. Mariana won't worry because she knows the child is with you,' he finished with a faintly ironical gleam.

Kate saw the two men look at one another with complete understanding, and wondered again at the strange nature of men. Randel could see Mariana's limitations, yet he still believed everything she told him.

The tea was an unqualified success. Kate could see that Mr. Lister was impressed by the way Rosa was completely at ease in the Villa Paradis, and Kate's face burned with embarrassment at the compliments she could hear Mrs. McCormack paying her, as she talked to Randel. Later it seemed easy for James to suggest that he propose Kate's name for admission to the English Club, and he looked over at Randel hesitantly. Mr. Lister immediately agreed and said he would second it, that he knew he should have done something about it, long ago.

Kate hesitated, looking at Rosa, who was engrossed in her usual fascinating hobby of making patterns with the buttons. James read her thoughts.

'Take Rosa along,' he said, with that easy assured manner of his. There are lots of children there and they have their own little playground. It's perfectly safe—paddling pool, sand pit, doll's house, swings.' He looked at Randel. 'I think Rosa needs some friends of her own age, don't you?'

Randel nodded, but Kate noticed that there was a questioning look on his face as he glanced round the lovely room. She wished she could guess his thoughts.

Randel walked back to the Pensio afterwards with Kate and Rosa, saw the Senhora, told her that he was buying Rosa some new clothes and that in future she could go to the sands, or the Club, or . . .

'The Club?' the Senhora had said, her voice rising slightly.

Kate could not help but overhear, for she

was on her way to the bathroom.

'Mees Williams belong to the Club?' the Senhora asked again.

Kate wondered why Mr. Lister sounded faintly uncomfortable as he said that Kate was going to be a member.

Now, as she drank in the beauty of the greeny-blue sky with the tiny golden crescent of a new moon suspended in it, the silhouetted palm trees and the string of bright lights sparkling along the bay, Kate hugged herself. It had been a wonderful day. Somewhere nearby, a bird rustled in the leaves of the trees. Who knew what results this day might not bring? She had heard Mrs. McCormack saying something about how much nicer it was for a child to live in a proper house with a garden and animals. And Mr. Lister had been very firm about the clothes for Rosa, and her expeditions, even though he had— eventually—taken Mariana, a sulky, dignified Mariana, out to dinner to smooth her hurt pride. Even that had given Kate a warm feeling of satisfaction, for Mr. Lister's eyes had been twinkling as he told her he would take Mariana out.

'As you said to me once, Kate, I must be the soul of discretion and not cause offence,' he said.

Back in her bedroom, Kate closed the mosquito netting and began to write one of her thrice-weekly letters to her mother.

Sometimes she was conscience-stricken because she was not homesick, yet she still worried about how her mother was managing. Despite her energy and cheerfulness, there were many things that were difficult to do from a wheelchair, and friends, while helping a great deal, were not the same as one's own child. Still, her mother wrote happily, and the only way Kate could do anything constructive was to write long chatty letters. Tonight's was easy, for there was so much to write. She wrote ten pages and then finished:

'It was odd seeing James and Mr. Lister together. They are so completely different. James is essentially a kind man—you have only to look at him to feel warm and safe. But perhaps a little dull? Somehow you always know what he will do, how he will react. He is a most wonderful friend, of course. Mr. Lister, now, is the opposite. You are always on edge with him, wondering how he will behave. He is a man of moods. Sometimes I could almost hit him for his stupidity, and the next moment I'm so sorry for him I could cry. He hasn't got a clue about children. He even asked me if I thought Rosa was "normal." I ask you, Mummy! Of course that is Mariana.

'I'm quite scared of her at times, for she seems prepared to stoop to anything. It is wonderful to know that now I can buy Rosa really pretty clothes and that I no longer have to do everything secretly. I'm getting Rosa some games so that I can teach her to count and spell. Mr. Lister remarked on the improvement in her English, and she no longer looks like a little *slug,* bless her.

'Oh, Mummy, this is a wonderful job! It's just that sometimes I catch myself shivering—just as if someone has walked over my grave. I caught the Senhora looking at me tonight and her glance was really evil. Aren't I being silly? Maybe it's just because she has such a malevolent sort of face and is always draped in black and her jet beads make a horrible noise as they dangle.'

Kate re-read the letter and then added a postscript.

'I'm a bit worried about my friend Natala. She hasn't been at the desk for three days now, so I'm wondering if she is ill. I'll ask one of the waiters in the morning. She is such a dear and so unhappy. She lives alone with her sick mother, so she may need some help. Take care of yourself—the six months will soon be gone and we shall be together again.'

As she signed the letter, Kate stifled a sigh. What would happen at the end of the six months? They would go back to England, and Mr. Lister would pay her, thank her politely, send Rosa to boarding school, and forget the whole episode.

Would she be able to forget it? Kate wondered. Hugging her knees, gazing into space, she admitted the truth to herself.

142

She was utterly, hopelessly, and helplessly in love with Randel Lister. More fool you, she told herself, as she set about preparing for bed. When a man had Mariana eating out of his hand, he would not look at anyone else! Who could blame him? Such beauty, such fire, such provocativeness, such a perpetual challenge to a man. Why—why, it was like the difference she felt between James and Mr. Lister. James was comforting and soothing—but Randel Lister was . . .

It was best not to think about it. She found a library book, curled up on her bed and began to read, deliberately shutting out tantalising, thrilling yet depressing thoughts of a lean, dark, arrogant man—a man of many moods.

In the morning she managed to see the manageress, a short fat woman in a very tight black frock with small white ringlets piled high on her head.

'She has gone,' Senhora Lopez said flatly when Kate asked about Natala.

It was a battle to get anything out of the woman, who was, quite obviously, unwilling to be co-operative. In the end, Kate was shocked to learn that Natala had been dismissed. When she pressed the manageress for a reason, the Senhora Lopez' dark eyes glittered and she had an ugly flush on her sallow skin.

'It was your fault—she was a good girl until you came and made her above herself. Then she lies, insults a guest, and so I said she must go.' She refused to give Kate Natala's address and told Kate that she had made trouble enough already.

Kate was both shocked and hurt—how could she have caused Natala's dismissal? As she went back to the flat, Mariana met her, and told her haughtily to prepare Rosa for a visit.

'I take her with me,' she told Kate.

Kate paused. 'Do you know why Natala was dismissed?' she asked.

She met the Portuguese girl's triumphant eyes and felt suddenly sick. She might have guessed it was Mariana's work.

'But of course I know,' Marina said smoothly. 'High time, too. She was impudent.'

Kate turned away. What could she say, or do, that could be effective? She dressed Rosa in silence, hardly noticing the little girl's curious glances. At the last moment, Kate held Rosa tight for a second, kissed her and whispered that she would see her soon and, in the meantime, to enjoy herself. Tea parties were always fun . . .

She was startled by Rosa's reaction. The small arms clung to her neck, her mouth was warm on Kate's cheek. 'Kate—never, never go away, please,' she begged, her eyes wide.

'I won't,' Kate promised, and whispered a silent *if I can help it.* Unfortunately so much seemed to depend on Mariana.

Kate stood for a long time after Mariana

and Rosa had gone out. What could she do? Could Mr. Lister help? Then she recalled that he had said he was going down to Durban for a few days. She went out into the heat of the day and took a bus, going to sit in the cool, quiet cathedral, trying to collect her thoughts.

What would happen to Natala? It would not be easy for her to get a job. As Natala said, people were embarrassed by her appearance. When Kate left the cool building, the heat of the street was even more powerful. Gasping a little, she hesitated and decided to have a long cool drink, sitting at one of the pavement cafés. She walked down the hot pavements, ignoring the glances, and the whistles. She had learned to cope with the many advances that every girl who walks alone in Lourenço Marques meets, and could even laugh at them now. She hesitated when she saw the face of a man she recognised, sitting outside one of the cafés. Even as she wondered if she dare risk asking him if he knew where Natala was, she left it too late to retreat. He was on his feet, hastening towards her, with that bold appraising smile she hated.

'Mees Williams!' He took her hand and raised it to his lips. His bold eyes looked her up and down. 'I am fortunate. You will join me?'

She sat down reluctantly, said she would like a cool drink, sipped it and listened while he paid her compliments, while his eyes said the things she knew he would like to say and which made her feel so uncomfortable, almost as if she had forgotten to dress properly that day. It was hard to interrupt his flow of conversation, harder still to bear the complacent looks he gave the other men at the little tables, as if to say *See—I have another slave!* Antonio reminded her irresistibly of a peacock—the next second she was ashamed. She must remember what Natala had said about him.

'Senhor Vidal,' Kate said firmly. 'Can you give me Natala's address?'

Antonio's mouth gaped open. He had been in the middle of a flowery, well-phrased, he thought, sentence, in praise of Kate's eyes, and she asked him a blunt question like that.

'Natala?' he said stupidly, and shrugged. 'Let us forget such a one. Our friendship with one another has the greatest importance.'

Kate flushed. She leaned forward, her voice hard. 'But I *am* worried about Natala. I want to know where she is, and . . .'

Someone stopped by their table. Kate looked up. It was James. The flood of thankfulness made her eyes glow warmly. 'Oh, James,' she said, not realising how she was betraying her relief, 'have you met Senhor Antonio Vidal?'

James was looking at the young Portuguese with cold eyes as he acknowledged the introduction and asked if he might join them.

146

Kate could have laughed at the way Antonio was scowling. He looked like a small boy who had been snubbed. James asked why Kate was looking so worried. Bless him, Kate thought, he was able to read her thoughts, for how else could he have known what cue to give her? If James knew that Antonio Vidal could find out Natala's address, he would make Antonio tell them.

But Antonio was sulking. He declared he did not know where Natala lived. That there was no need to be worried, for she was a good book-keeper and would get another position without difficulty.

'I don't agree,' Kate said emphatically. 'I know she was terrified of losing her job.' She turned to James. 'Mariana got her dismissed,' she said accusingly.

She was startled by James's reaction.

'Isn't that rather a rash statement?' he asked.

She stared at him—so he too, for all he had said, was under Mariana's spell. 'Perhaps it was,' she said, feeling as usual that it was just a waste of time trying to fight Mariana. 'But I'm still worried about Natala.'

James looked at his watch. 'My mother wants to see you, Kate. May I run you home?' He apologised for interrupting the little talk she had been having with Antonio. 'I'm sure that we can count on Senhor Vidal to help us trace your friend now that he knows how anxious you are.'

Kate saw Antonio's eyes flicker and had a moment of hope. James went on talking with his authoritative air. 'As Miss Williams's friend, I am naturally interested and would appreciate any help you can give us,' he finished formally.

Kate stood up and felt happier, for in other words, James was offering a bribe. This might work where all Kate's pleading must fail.

James dropped her off at the Pensio. 'Mother is out, but I guessed you needed rescuing,' he said with a friendly grin. At Kate's fervent assurance that he was right, he cautioned her to be careful. 'It's playing with fire, Kate. You may think you can handle men of Vidal's calibre, but believe me, you can't.'

She looked up into his troubled face. 'I do realise that, James. I'm very careful. I just happened to run into him, that's all. Natala is desperately in love with him, poor girl, and that's why I'm sure he knows where she is.'

James nodded. 'So am I. Well, we'll see what happens. I'll let you know if he contacts me.'

Mariana brought Rosa back to the flat very late indeed. Mariana was in a temper. 'Rosa— she has lost all her good behaviour. She was rude. You teach her the rudeness, like you teach all her friends,' she said, almost viciously, her eyes glinting. 'I do not like to go out with cheeky children.'

Kate's arms were round Rosa. She looked

148

up. 'Rosa is never cheeky,' she protested.

'You do not see it—for you are very cheeky, too,' Mariana told her, dark eyes flashing. She paused in the doorway. 'I tell Senhor Lister this and he agree. He says all English girls are cheeky—it is their way.' She smiled acidly. 'He said it is a peety. Men like the girls to have the good manners. That is why English men love Portuguese girls.'

She closed the door with a bang. Biting her lip, feeling the helpless anger fill her, Kate devoted herself to the tired, tearful Rosa. Later that night Rosa had a nightmare. This time everything was different, for she clung to Kate, and when she saw Mariana in the doorway screamed louder than ever.

Mariana was furious, but kept her voice scathingly cold as she requested Kate to stop the child screaming, for they would have complaints if they disturbed the Pensio's night. When they were alone Rosa stopped crying, but still clung to Kate, so finally Kate carried the child to her own room, and Rosa slept in Kate's bed, cheeks still wet, one hand clutching Kate's.

Next day Kate got a clue as to the reason for the nightmare. They were talking Portuguese, and Rosa said in one of those pedantic little phrases she was slowly forgetting, 'You are making the improvement, Kate.'

'Thanks to you, darling,' Kate said, and bent and kissed the child. She was startled by the

149

fervour of Rosa's return kiss.

'Kate,' Rosa begged, 'don't ever leave me!'

'I'll never leave you,' Kate promised, and wondered if she ought to say that. If only she could be sure it was true! Yet there must come a time . . . If only she could stay with Rosa long enough to give her a sense of security.

In the days ahead, Kate tried to find out why Rosa was once more afraid. Mrs. McCormack had invited them ceremoniously to lunch. Mrs. McCormack had behaved very formally—and politely—towards the Dominguez. She had visited the Senhora and also invited her to an evening of bridge. The Senhora had been visibly impressed, and had several times asked Kate questions about James—his age, his job, was he the heir? Amused, Kate began to wonder if perhaps Mariana was weighing the advantages of marrying James, as against those she would enjoy if she married Randel. Kate, of course, knew that she herself would not hesitate—but then she chose with her heart and not her mind. If she had any sense, Kate felt she should choose James. So good and kind, so wonderfully understanding—yet such fun to be with; he would be a husband in a million. Yet with her foolish heart she had only to hear Randel's footsteps—his voice—or meet his eyes across a room to know without fail whom she loved.

Sometimes unrequited love is sad and hard

to endure, but Kate found she enjoyed it. Maybe it was because she did not really hope—she simply dreamed. Dreams were free. She could dream of their home—a white villa surrounded by flowers, Randel coming home at the end of the day, Rosa teaching her small stepsisters to talk . . . Kate would stop thinking then, and sigh. It was just a lovely dream. She suffered from no illusions. Randel had never seen her as anything but a pleasant young girl, who might be useful, and who had proved quite successful at looking after his problem daughter. Another thing that puzzled her was that though she could have such tender thoughts of Randel, could tremble when he was near with a sweet breathlessness she had never known before, yet Kate could be so angry with him—just for a single remark—that she almost exploded.

Such an occasion arose soon after his return from Durban. He took her out to tea at the English Club and they sat on the terrace, under palm trees and with distant strains of music. Young people lounged round the pool, Rosa was playing with a doll by Kate's feet.

Kate was happy, just to look across the table at that lean handsome face. She took a deep breath.

'Kate,' Randel said coldly, and frowned. Kate woke up from her dream. 'Kate, I don't want to seem difficult, but Mariana tells me . . .'

151

She stared at him, wondering if he had noticed how her head had instantly been lifted, that she was immediately on the defensive. 'Mariana tells you?' Then she remembered Rosa and looked down. 'Another time,' Kate murmured.

They played with their tea. It was a relief when a small girl with red hair came to Rosa and asked her to dig a hole. The two children knew one another slightly, and with great solemnity Rosa stood up and asked Kate for permission to go with Flora.

'Of course, darling,' Kate said, and waited until the children were out of earshot. Then she braced herself, turning to her employer. 'Well?' she asked.

He watched Rosa walk away. 'She asked your permission to go,' he said in surprise. 'Mariana said she had lost her manners.'

Kate counted ten, and then was proud of her moderate voice. 'Perhaps we have different standards—Mariana and I. I think she calls it good manners when a child is willing to sit for hours in a corner of the room while adults talk and forget her. When she does not interrupt her elders or make a nuisance of herself.' Against her every effort, Kate's voice began to tremble. 'Rosa, I'm afraid, has grown used to English ways. She talks to people. I realise she must have changed.' She saw that he was staring at her, frowning. Was she being very aggressive? But she must defend Rosa. Then she forgot to try to be calm, cool and collected.

'Mr. Lister, how can we go on like this?' she said, almost desperately. 'You distrust everything I do. You look at Rosa through a microscope, searching for faults. Can't you see . . . or *won't* you see—' she did not realise she was shaking her finger in his face—'that Rosa needs love, love, more love? She can't have enough. She needs praise, encouragement. Never has she known security. Mariana says Rosa clings to me now. Once she clung to Anna. But now I am with her all day long. I am the one she trusts.' She was suddenly aware that she was almost shouting. She looked round nervously, but luckily no one was near them. She dared not meet his eyes, for her courage would go and these things must be said. 'She had a nightmare—but only after she had been out with Mariana. I know she was over-tired, but I think many adults forget how much a child hears and understands.' Kate drew a long shuddering breath. Here it came! 'I can tell you why Rosa was so afraid of me when I arrived. She told Mrs. McCormack that I was going to take her to London to chop off her head.'

Now she looked at him. He was quiet, not angry at all, she saw. But he looked as if he did not believe a word she had said.

'Chop off her head? That's ridiculous.'

Kate sighed. She felt the inspiration

trickling out of her. Why waste time? 'Maybe she heard a story about the Princes in the Tower—of how King Henry the Eighth beheaded his wives . . . Mrs. McCormack thought someone might have read her an historical story.'

Mr. Lister said slowly, almost thoughtfully, 'I don't imagine anyone ever read a story to Rose until you came.'

Kate stared at him. Was he angry? His face betrayed nothing. He offered her a cigarette and lighted it. The little act gave her time to calm down. She waited nervously for his reaction. None came. They talked of other things, and then he said it was time to go and she called Rosa.

It was as he drove them back to the Pensio that he said something relevant to their conversation. 'I'm beginning to understand a lot of things that puzzled me before, Kate.'

He gave her that thrilling, breathtaking smile that made her life worth living just because she could wait for the miracle of it.

'Keep on with the good work, Kate, you'll educate me yet,' he told her.

She went up the stairs with wings on her feet, sang as she bathed Rosa. It was long after Rosa was asleep that the Senhora sent a message that Kate was wanted on the telephone.

She ran down the corridor, expecting it to be James or his mother, hoping without hope

154

that it might be Randel.

It was Antonio Vidal.

'You wish to see Natala? I will call for you in fifteen minutes,' he said. And rang off.

Kate hesitated. Yet if he knew where Natala was . . . She saw the time and frowned. Natala must be ill—otherwise why the haste?

She changed her dress quickly, told the Senhora she was going out, and ran down to the hall. She saw that she was early.

Suddenly she was afraid. James had warned her, she remembered. On an impulse she went to the telephone, dialling the McCormacks' number. Mrs. McCormack answered. Kate asked swiftly for James, but he was out. She was going to explain when she heard the sound of the car outside. She did not want Antonio to think she doubted him—he had such funny moods that he might turn sulky and refuse to help. So she said breathlessly, and very worriedly, that it didn't really matter, and when Antonio walked in he found her sitting patiently on a chair.

CHAPTER X

Kate sat at the table in the corner of the dark, smoke-filled cellar and gazed around with alarm. Antonio had told her it was called the Matador Club. Nearly everyone there was a man—they sat in groups, close together, hardly talking, drinking steadily, their dark faces and deep glowering eyes lifting suspiciously when a newcomer entered the room.

She had danced twice with Antonio and had then pleaded a headache. He sat opposite her, his dark eyes fixed on hers, an inscrutable look in them. Kate had hated dancing with him. The dance floor was so small that they hardly moved, and Antonio held her so close that she could hardly breathe. The last straw had come when he had turned and bitten her arm.

It was a gentle bite—but a bite, nevertheless. She had shied like a frightened horse and jerked herself free.

'I don't care to dance any more,' she had said. 'My head aches.'

As they sat down, he refilled her glass with a sharp, bitter red wine. Then he toasted her, his eyes mocking.

'You Engleesh girls are the teasers,' he said.

Kate stared at him, puzzled, then thought she understood. Her cheeks grew hot. Did he think, because she had come out with him tonight to look for Natala, that she was encouraging him? That she was prepared to—

'Where is Natala?' she demanded abruptly. 'I don't believe she would come to a place like this.'

She looked round again. The air was thick with smoke. Suddenly someone shouted and a bottle sailed through the air, to crash against the wall.

Kate sat, frozen stiff with horror. She wanted to get up, yet was afraid to move lest she be involved in trouble. She stared at Antonio again and saw that he was amused by her panic. She leaned forward and said slowly, 'Where is Natala?'

He flicked the ash off his cigarette airily. 'If you are a good girl, I will tell you. If not . . . I won't.' He smiled mockingly.

Kate sat back. How could she have been such a fool as to trust him? If only . . .

It was no good regretting what she had done. Now she must find a way to get out of here. It could not be done by antagonising him.

The whole evening had simply been a trap to make her go out with him. And she had walked into it! He had driven down town fast, telling her they would see Natala at once. Then in that crowded room, the air filled with smoke and the sound of noisy laughter, they had danced, Antonio keeping up the pretence

157

of looking for Natala.

'She has a friend—they come here every night,' he told Kate. She tried to imagine Natala in such a place and failed. Yet Antonio seemed sure.

They had gone through the hot black night to another noisy place, this time being whisked aloft in a lift to a rooftop where the glorious sea with its circle of dancing lights made a never-to-be-forgotten picture. They danced again, and when Kate got restless, Antonio said that the Matador Club must be the one and he had made a mistake. He had been humble, apologetic, or she might have insisted, then, on going home.

Now she wondered how to do it. They sat silently staring at one another. Antonio looked triumphant, and Kate tried to hide her dismay. This was a foreign land—suppose Antonio turned unpleasant? How could she cope? She might have to walk home through the darkness. Mrs. McCormack had once said that on each street corner lurked a bandit with a long curved knife. Maybe she had said it to frighten Kate, but Kate remembered it.

'Antonio—' she began desperately.

He leant forward and took her hand. She fought the desire to snatch it free—made herself smile a little, and then . . .

Things happened!

Across the room two men were suddenly shouting insults—a table was overturned. A

158

chair flew through the air, crashing noisily in a group of people, who leapt to their feet, screaming angrily. Two men were fighting, surrounded by a group of men who shouted encouragement.

Kate was on her feet, back pressed to the wall, her hand to her mouth in terror. She saw Antonio's face—he was white, too, staring in dismay at the fracas.

And then, miraculously, James was there, taking her arm, swinging her into the circle of his, holding her close as he pushed his way through the crowd. Even as she felt the tears of relief flowing down her cheeks, she saw, to her amazement, Randel following them, his face grim, his fingers hooked round Antonio's arm—a struggling, frightened Antonio, who looked completely helpless in Randel's firm grasp.

They all piled into the car, and before Kate realised it she was being led by James, his arm round her shoulder, into a big room. It was obviously Mr. Lister's, for, as he almost threw Antonio into a chair, he said curtly:

'I think we all need a drink.'

Kate's hand shook as she tried to sip the whisky he gave her. He looked down at her coldly.

'Drink it up,' he ordered.

She obeyed, and the strong drink burned her throat. But she felt better and the trembling ceased. She was aware of the silence

159

in the room, of Antonio trying to make himself so small in the chair that no one would see him. Of James's kind, curious eyes. Of Randel's cold, hostile ones.

Randel Lister spoke first.

'When I was told you had gone dancing with this . . . man—' his finger made a contemptuous gesture towards the crouching, terrified Portuguese—'I refused to believe it. You told me yourself that . . .'

'I know,' Kate said quickly. Mariana again, of course. But perhaps it was as well that she *had* told Randel, otherwise they might never have rescued her. 'It wasn't to go dancing with him—'

They listened in silence as she told them the whole story. James began to laugh.

'Honestly, Kate, you swallow every story. How could you be so stupid?' His voice was kind, and she did not mind his amusement.

'I hadn't time to think—I tried to get you on the phone . . .'

Randel frowned. 'You telephoned McCormack?' He sounded annoyed. Maybe he thought she should have telephoned him. She had never thought of it. She stared at him wonderingly. Did that mean something—that she had not thought of Randel when she was in trouble? She thought only of James.

She turned wondering eyes first at James and then at Randel, not realising she was doing so. She was asking herself a question. If she loved Randel, why hadn't she thought of him?

'We could have traced this girl through the police,' Randel went on impatiently. 'It seems rather foolish to risk your neck with a ruffian of this type just for an acquaintance.'

'Natala is her friend,' James put in quietly, and smiled at Kate. 'That's different, eh, Kate?'

Randel was frowning again. 'It was by sheer chance that McCormack and I bumped into one another. I didn't like the idea of you mixed up with such a man as Vidal, and apparently McCormack had a feeling—'

'Kate rang my mother, who said she had behaved oddly. Mother left a note by my bed. I went to sleep, had a bad dream about Kate, woke up, re-read the note and decided to do something about it,' James said cheerfully, as if it was the most natural procedure in the world. He met Randel's long thoughtful gaze for a silent moment and then smiled. 'We're very fond of Kate, you know, Lister.'

Randel's mouth twisted. 'So I see,' he remarked.

James stood up, his big body moving with a leisurely grace. He walked to Antonio, lifted him by his collar gently and put him on his feet. He grinned at Kate. 'I'll have that address for you in five minutes. We'll find your friend tomorrow.'

'Oh, James, you're so good!' Kate watched

him march the unfortunate—as her soft heart now called him—Antonio outside. Her eyes shone. James was wonderful!

Randel Lister spoke curtly. 'Honestly, Kate, you alarm me. You walk into trouble without even noticing it. A good thing for you we came on the scene then. It could have been very ugly.'

'I am sorry,' she said earnestly. 'I'm afraid I act before I think. But I'm so worried about Natala, and he promised . . .'

'You mustn't believe everything a man tells you,' Randel said crossly. He looked at her and she saw, with a sudden sweet breathlessness, that he was really concerned about her. 'You'll get hurt, and . . .'

James came back, grinning. 'That's okay. I'll pick you up just after lunch, Kate, and we'll go together and see your friend. I may be able to help her get another job.'

Kate was on her feet, clasping her hands with youthful excitement, her eyes shining as she stared up at him. 'Oh, James, I don't know what I'd do without you!'

The two men had a short argument as to who should drive Kate home. She stood waiting patiently, wishing the little argument was not merely a polite one and that both men really wanted to see her home. James had common sense on his side, for he had to go home, anyhow—so Kate said good night to a suddenly cool Randel Lister and went off with James.

He walked up to the dark flat with her and saw her safely inside.

'Tomorrow afternoon,' he said, and held her hands tightly. She looked up at him.

'Oh, James, I don't know how to thank you.'

'Then don't,' he said, smiling. For one moment he looked as if he had been going to kiss her. She was glad when he did not. Somehow she did not feel she wanted James to kiss her. Yet she liked him so much, had turned to him automatically when she was in trouble.

The following day they found Natala. Kate and James walked down a narrow lane between two high walls and found themselves in a small paved yard. There was a hut with a curtained window and closed door. James knocked several times and, when there was no answer, forced it open.

A wave of damp, dusty heat hit them. As their eyes grew accustomed to the darkness they saw two beds. In one was Natala, with dark frightened eyes, in the other a small, wizened-looking little woman lay still.

'Kate!' Natala cried, and then began to sob—dreadful shaking sobs that racked Kate as she held her friend close and tried to comfort her.

They learned that Natala had fallen and could not move, that her mother had somehow got her to bed, then had one of her frequent heart attacks, managing to crawl round the room until the last of their food was gone.

James acted swiftly. Soon an ambulance arrived to take Natala and her mother to hospital. He told Natala not to worry about the expense.

'You can pay me back,' he said, judging instantly that charity would be an insult. Kate looked at him with wonder. James sensed everything. 'I'll help you find a much better job,' he grinned at Natala.

Natala grabbed his hand and kissed it. 'You are too good!' she murmured brokenly.

He patted her head clumsily. 'You are Kate's friend—and therefore mine.'

Natala clung to Kate's hand, but no one was allowed to go with her in the ambulance.

'We'll come and see you,' Kate promised, and watched the vehicle drive off with tears running down her cheeks.

'Hey!' James said. 'Why cry now? Everything will be all right.'

'But it might not have been.'

He walked back to the Pensio with her, where he had left his car.

'No,' he said gravely. 'It might not have been. Had it not been for your insistence on finding where she lived, they could both have died of starvation.'

'Oh, James!' Kate looked up at him and shivered. 'What a dreadful thought!'

'It is.' He looked grim. 'Awful to think they

164

had no friends, no neighbours. I'll go along later to the hospital and give you a ring, Kate.'

Rosa was awake when Kate got upstairs. She was sitting in the middle of the bed, very still. When she saw Kate, she launched herself over the room, clinging to Kate. 'I thought you'd gone . . . gone for ever,' she kept saying.

Kate held her close, rocking her a little. 'I've promised you I'll not go, my poppet.'

Rosa would not be comforted for a long time. It was when they were out for a walk through the park that she said without warning, 'You tell the truth, Kate, don't you? You think it wrong not to tell the truth?'

Kate looked at the small, earnest face. 'I always tell the truth,' she said steadily. Which was true, for Kate was not one to tell a lie lightly and would only do it to save a person from pain.

Rosa looked at her. 'Mariana says she is going to be my new mother. Is that true?'

Kate stared at her, her face rigid with dismay. Mariana would surely not dare to say such a thing to Rosa unless it was true.

'I don't know, darling,' Kate said slowly. 'I can't say if it is true or not. Why don't you ask your father?'

Rosa shook her head violently. They walked on for a while, then Rosa looked up. 'Kate, why don't you ask my father to marry you? Then you could be my new mother.'

There was something so wistful in the young

face that Kate forgot she was in a public park. She dropped on her knees on the grass, put her arms round Rosa, her cheek against hers, and said with all the honesty in her, 'Oh, my darling, how I wish I could. There's nothing I would rather be than your new mother.'

'Indeed?' a cold, sarcastic voice said. 'That may be true, but is it wise to tell the world?'

Her cheeks scarlet, Kate scrambled to her feet and found herself staring into Mrs. Kelly's face. For a moment she wondered who the woman was—then remembered the inquisitive woman who had cross-examined her on the ship the day they arrived, and for whom Mrs. McCormack had such amazing sympathy.

Now Kate looked into Mrs. Kelly's eyes and saw that this was a very sick woman indeed. A white-faced woman, trembling a little. Kate made her voice cordial.

'How nice to see you, Mrs. Kelly. Look—there's a seat here. Shall we sit down?'

Her hand under Mrs. Kelly's elbow, Kate led the way over the grass. It was a relief to see Mrs. Kelly sit down safely. Rosa was by Kate's side, her face curious.

It took Mrs. Kelly some time to recover her voice. Then she smiled—a gaunt, wolfish smile that frightened Kate and made her glance down anxiously at Rosa. But Rosa had wandered off and was gazing into a small fish pond, her soft pretty hair falling forward. Kate felt her usual rush of grateful wonder because

166

Rosa looked so different these days. But she was startled when Mrs. Kelly echoed her thoughts.

'She's a different child,' Mrs. Kelly said. 'I made a point of seeing her soon after you took charge, and I thought, "That quiet, weak girl will never be able to do anything for that unfortunate child."' Mrs. Kelly's dark eyes looked at Kate curiously. 'You have more stamina than I guessed. I congratulate you.'

Kate blushed with pleasure. 'Thank you,' she said gratefully.

Mrs. Kelly's smile vanished swiftly. 'Now I'm going to give you some advice that you won't like. Don't think about Randel Lister. He is not for you.'

Kate gasped. It was the last thing she had expected Mrs. Kelly to say.

Mrs. Kelly went on slowly, 'I have been ill—but I hear things. The Dominguez are strange folk. There are rumours. Ugly talk—' she shook her head as if trying to shake away bad dreams. 'I have heard things. They hate you—they will not hesitate . . .'

Poor old thing, Kate thought with quick sympathy. Obviously she has had a nervous breakdown and now has a mania about the Dominguez. True, Kate felt ill at ease and a little fearful with them, but danger? Oh, no, that was an exaggeration!

Mrs. Kelly put her hand on Kate's arm, and Kate nearly jumped out of her skin. Despite the great heat and the way Kate's dress stuck to her wet body, Mrs. Kelly's hand was icy cold. Her eyes blazed into Kate's.

'I'm warning you. They mean to get Randel Lister, and nothing will stop them. If you have any sense, you'll let them see that you're not interested in them.' Those strange, frightening eyes searched Kate's face. 'You're in love with him, aren't you?'

Kate's cheeks were aflame. 'I . . .'

Mrs. Kelly stood up, holding on to the seat as she began to walk unsteadily away, then turned round and said in a truly frightening voice, 'If you don't mind what happens to *you*—then think about the child. She could be involved, too.'

Kate watched Mrs. Kelly's unsteady progress and wondered if she should run after her to help her. But Rosa was absorbed in watching the goldfish, and Mrs. Kelly had seemed all right before she talked such rubbish. But was it rubbish? Kate was remembering some of the things Natala had said. About the Dominguez reputation—their few friends the way people eyed them curiously.

It was nonsense. Of course it was. Melodramatic nonsense. She got up swiftly and went to Rosa's side, to watch with her the small shiny bodies of the little fishes.

James called for Kate that night and took her to his house, saying his mother would be back before she need leave. He told her he had seen Natala; she would be all right, but unfortunately her fall and the lack of treatment immediately afterwards might make her spastic condition worse.

'They have a new method of treatment, however, which they are going to try out,' he finished. Natala's mother was very sick. In fact, the worst was anticipated. James met Kate's concerned eyes. 'I think Natala has always known that one day her mother would be too weak to outlast these repeated attacks,' he said gently.

They talked that evening as they had never talked before. Kate, relieved about Natala, could relax, although running all the time through her mind was the thought of Rosa's question about Mariana—and Mrs. Kelly's warning.

James told her about the vast business his father had built up, starting as he had done with one small native store. She asked him casually if he was the heir or owned the whole concern. She wondered at his quizzical glance and was embarrassed when he said chidingly, 'Oh, no, Kate, not you too. Trying to find out if I'm worth marrying?' His eyes were twinkling, yet there was a gravity about his voice that surprised her.

'Of course not. It's . . . it's just that the Senhora asked me the other day.'

James looked quite relieved. 'Oh, Mariana!

That's understandable. She's trying to find a rich husband, of course.'

'I heard you were a millionaire,' Kate said naïvely.

James laughed. 'I am—in a way. It's all mine. My father made it over to me, knowing he could leave Mother safely in my hands. She's such a scatterbrain, bless her, and has the most generous heart. She would have given the whole lot away if I wasn't here to stop her.'

'James,' Kate said carefully, 'do you think Mr. Lister is going to marry Mariana?'

James stared at her as if he could read her thoughts. 'I don't know,' he admitted. 'I think she's playing the field—and getting a little desperate about it.' He came and lighted a cigarette for Kate, looked at the clock, remarked that his mother must be winning at bridge to be so late, and that he would drive Kate home soon, for she must be tired after such an emotional day, and then went on—answering Kate's question. 'You see, Kate, I can't help being sorry for the girl. Mariana, I mean,' he added with a quick smile. 'She is old for a Portuguese girl to be single. Also her mother does not move in the right circles so she can't have a "good" marriage arranged for her. That means she has to turn to a foreigner. I believe there is a sugar planter, Randel Lister and myself. We're the three favourites at the moment. People bet on us.' He laughed at Kate's shocked face. 'Kate dear, you are naïve.

170

This is such a small place, we all know one another's business and have no secrets. At the moment I think the betting is highest on me.'

Kate stood up. 'I think that's awful,' she said, shocked to the core. 'People watching you, discussing you, betting on your romances. Do *you* think Randel wants to marry Mariana?' she asked James point-blank.

She wondered why he stared at her so thoughtfully, why his eyes were so kind and sympathetic, why he took so long answering her.

'I don't know,' he said heavily. 'Men are queer creatures, Kate. You can know a woman is selfish, ruthless, hard—and you can still be enslaved by her charm, bewitched by her so that unless you are near her you are not alive. Your reasoning power can come into action and you ask yourself important questions: What hope of happiness have you together? None, you decide, this must end.' He smiled, a little bitterly. 'Then you see her again—and *phut!* All your ideas and theories are wiped out. You just know you can't live without her— no matter what it costs you.'

There was silence as he finished, a silence that seemed to stretch for ever as she stared at him in dismay. So James felt like that about Mariana, as well. Kate turned away, her eyes stinging with tears. What hope had she? What hope had she ever had?

'Please take me home,' she said in a quiet

little voice. 'I'm very tired.' Tired—or heartsick? What did it matter? If James had said he felt like that about Mariana—how much more bewitched must Randel be?

CHAPTER XI

Kate's life settled into a very pleasant rhythm. It was fun to go to the English Club and have an occasional game of tennis and talk to other girls, to watch Rosa mixing with children, to see her skin become glowing and warmly brown, to have her sleep without nightmares. Even Kate's anxiety about Natala was lifting, for each visit showed the Portuguese girl's health to be improving. Unfortunately Natala blamed herself for her mother's grave condition and kept saying that if only she hadn't fallen, her mother need not have got out of bed.

'I am so clumsee,' Natala would say, her eyes full of tears.

Kate had the surprise of her life when James said casually that he was organising a holiday on his yacht. She stared at him wide-eyed. She had not known he owned one! Later she wondered if his mother was not behind the idea, for Mrs. McCormack was so gleeful about it that Kate could not help thinking there was a 'plan' in her mind.

Kate and Rosa, Randel and Mariana, James and his mother—those were the guests. Kate felt almost sorry for Mariana when she saw how surprised and thrilled she was by the invitation. Not even the thought of Kate being included could dampen her excitement, and Kate could hear Mariana and her mother talking for hours about the forthcoming trip, and wondered a little at Mariana's high spirits. Natala smiled understandingly and said:

'You do not see? This means to Mariana that James's mother has accepted her. It is not easy for girls like Mariana to be included in such an intimate family party.'

It did not make sense to Kate. It was just an invitation. But then she had never grasped the intricacies of the Portuguese social customs.

It was a lovely yacht, Kate thought. She had never been on one before. A cabin cruiser, it had a motor as well as sails. There were four small, well furnished cabins and a surprisingly large amount of deck space. The day they set out was hot, the sky pale, the Indian Ocean a deep blue. Kate, with Rosa on her knee, sat with Mrs. McCormack and watched James and Randel behaving like happy small boys as they pulled first one rope and then another and sailors swarmed about.

'I hope they know what they're doing,' Kate said.

Mrs. McCormack laughed with delight. 'My dear Kate, you sound just like an anxious mother!'

Kate felt something like one as she watched Randel leaning over the edge. There were sharks in the water—supposing he fell in?

Mariana was standing near the two men, her long, lovely body revealed in her slim pleated skirt and thin blouse, her head thrown back, her eyes wide with admiration as she glanced from one of them to the other. Mrs. McCormack sighed and looked at Kate significantly.

'She certainly knows how to make the most of her assets,' Mrs. McCormack said in a low voice.

Kate turned to look at the Portuguese girl and saw the way Randel was laughing down at her. 'She has so many assets,' Kate replied.

Rosa was fascinated by everything, even though still a little afraid the boat would suddenly sink and they would all be battling with sharks! Kate showed her the lifebelts, explained that there was a dinghy to be lowered, told her that James and Rosa's father could both swim well, and that so could she.

Rosa smiled rather doubtfully and clung even more tightly to Kate's hand. They watched a sailor swarm up the rigging, and gradually, beautifully the sails unfolded, billowing out, snow-white and clean. The boat heeled over a little and Rosa's fingers clutched Kate's convulsively as the boat sped along the empty bay, past the sand dunes.

After lunch, everyone but Kate took a siesta. Her natural energy made it impossible for her to lie down, despite the heat. Besides, on the deck, there was a lovely breeze. She found a chair and enjoyed the joyous motion of the boat as it danced—no, flew along, sending up a fine spray. She was surprised when Randel appeared and sat down beside her. They sat silently for a while.

'How much nicer this is than working in an office,' Kate said dreamily, thinking of her life in London, the fight to work each day, the long hours, the fight home again, the lonely evenings. 'James says he would like to live on a desert island.'

'Easy enough for James to talk,' Randel said in a dry voice. 'When you're practically a millionaire, it's easy. Money is only important to those who don't possess any.'

'Is money so important?' She was comfortably relaxed, not seeing him as her employer—not even as the man she loved.

She was startled by the violence of his reply, and listened as he told her something of his youth. She had known nothing of his background before, and she sat, breathlessly still, hoping that no one would interrupt them. His father had been injured in a car crash, and died after five years of pain. His mother had educated her three sons and then had also died, while Randel was still at school.

'The doctor told me I was old enough to use

my eyes. My mother died of—well, he called it politely malnutrition, but he meant starvation,' Randel said bitterly. 'He said I should have left school, given up my high-faluting ideas and gone to work. Looking back, I see he was right. But Mother was so keen to see us get on—so ambitious, so pleased when I won the scholarship. I never thought of the extras, clothes, etc. We were always shabby—in the holidays I worked. But you see, Kate, I have known real poverty. I think that's what drives me so hard. I'm determined that Rosa will never have to suffer as my mother did. I am investing the money for her so that she will never want.

Kate stared at him, seeing the young boy, stricken by his mother's death, tortured by the doctor's callous words. Yet was Randel right? Wouldn't it be better for Rosa to know her father now than to have a safe future?

'And you, Kate, have you ever been hungry?' Randel asked her, his voice dry.

She almost hated him when he spoke in that voice. It made her feel very young and naïve, delegating her to her correct place. How did he talk when he was alone with Mariana? She tried to imagine his deep thrilling voice becoming husky with emotion, those eyes that could be so cool and critical becoming warm and ardent.

She sighed. 'We were so happy. Never rich but never poor. Then Mother caught polio and nearly died, but recovered. She always managed to laugh and Dada adored her, waiting on her hand and foot. Then—then just over a year ago, he died. It wasn't easy to manage on our own, but . . . but Mother has enough to live on and . . . it's just that we miss him so terribly.' She looked at the sea through blurred eyes. 'I do realise how lucky I was to have such a happy childhood. It makes all the difference to your outlook on life.'

'I quite agree. I wish Rosa could have it.'

Kate looked at him. For once they were close, sharing an unusual intimacy. It gave her courage to say, 'Have you never thought of marrying again?'

He stared at her, narrowing his eyes. He smiled, tolerantly, as if she was a child. 'It's not as simple as that, Kate. No marriage merely for the sake of Rose could succeed. There must be love—real, lasting love.'

Before she could speak, Mariana's voice interrupted. 'Ah, Randel—you promised to show me the ship.' She stood there, now in white shorts, a coral shirt making her hair darker and more lovely than ever, her full red mouth provocative. 'It is the business talk you have with Kate, eh? Now that is over—let us have fun!' She held out her long, slim, olive-coloured hand to him.

With a quick half-apologetic smile at Kate, Randel took Mariana's hand and stood up. They walked down the deck, lightly swinging hands, Mariana looking up at him laughingly. As they turned, she looked over her shoulder for a brief mocking smile at Kate. Kate sighed and turned her attention to the sea.

Maybe she had misjudged Randel. Maybe it was his hard, unhappy youth—his battle with his conscience. Obviously Mariana represented glamorous romance to him—and of course, being his wife's sister made her a sort of relation.

That started a line of thought in her mind. A man's wife's sister . . . She must ask James some time.

But then, of course, Randel would know all about that. Randel was clever.

Later, sitting under the awning James had rigged against the sun, Kate and Mrs. McCormack had one of their frequent talks on love and living. Mrs. McCormack was feeling restless, for once she was crocheting furiously, glancing up every now and then to look down the deck to where Mariana was with the two men, telling their fortunes with cards, her deep laugh ringing out, her eyes flashing as she kept the two men interested.

'How stupid can men be, Kate?' Mrs. McCormack asked irritably.

Kate chuckled. Rosa was lying by her side, carefully cutting out pictures from a magazine.

'It depends on the temptation, I suppose,' she replied. She felt quite gay and happy, content to bask in the sun, in the unusual luxury of being near Randel for so many days, and even the obvious fact that Mariana was drawing both men to her side more securely than ever failed to worry Kate. In any case, she had long ago accepted her love for Randel as hopeless.

What simple girl could compete with such a beauty as Mariana? She said this so often to herself that sometimes Kate thought the words must be etched on her heart. She used them if she dared hope because he smiled at her, or on an occasion, like the night before, when Randel had danced with her on the slightly rolling deck, in the perfectly still night, with the stars twinkling in that wonderful sky, the sea glimmering with phosphorescence. The soft romantic music filled the air as they drifted to the music of a waltz, her eyes half-closed, pretending they were on their honeymoon. But then Mariana had come over, saying the next was a tango and she had promised Randel to teach him the Portuguese way to do it.

Now Kate's thoughts came back to the present to hear the end of Mrs. McCormack's sentence, 'but you don't think James is *serious,* dear child?'

Kate opened her eyes, smiled at her friend and looked at James. He was leaning forward with that sweet, friendly smile of his, his eyes amused as he teased Mariana.

'I don't know,' Kate said thoughtfully,

remembering a certain conversation she had had with James. 'Honestly I don't know.'

'Oh dear, I do hope not,' Mrs. McCormack said in such a distressed voice that Kate turned to her at once. 'Oh, Kate, I know I'm silly, but dear, I am so very fond of you, and James thinks you are such a nice girl and . . . Kate, you do like James very much, don't you?'

'Very much indeed,' Kate said warmly and with truth. 'I think James is wonderful—the most wonderful man I ever met.'

As she finished speaking, someone sat in a chair by her side. She turned her head. It was Randel. Had he heard her words? But he was not looking at her, he was bending to pick up some pictures Rosa had cut out, was speaking to his daughter in a slightly nervous placating way that made Kate's heart yearn for him. Life was not easy for him.

The next day they dropped anchor in a small bay, and everyone, except Mrs. McCormack who elected to stay on board, changed into swim suits and was rowed ashore to the lovely curved beach with its fine white sand and cliffs towering above them. Kate and Rosa began collecting the beautiful strands of blue, green and even purple seaweed and to collect sea shells.

'Kate! Kate!' Rosa called excitedly, and Kate lay down and peered into the clear pools to see the small transparent fishes, the little scuttling crabs.

'Kate,' Rosa asked suddenly, and looked up, her eyes bright, her hand clutching a rosy pink shell, 'what is a burden?'

It was a strange word for a little girl to use. Kate hesitated. 'It—it's an obligation—something one has to do.'

'But doesn't want to?' Rosa asked brightly. Kate looked round. They were alone; Mariana and the two men were walking towards the water.

'Yes,' Kate said reluctantly. 'Why?'

'Mariana told someone I was a burden and she hated burdens,' Rosa told her.

Kate caught her breath. 'Oh, darling, I think you must have heard the wrong word. No one could call you a burden. Why, we love you.'

Rosa scooped up a tiny fish and then let it go, again, chuckling with glee. 'Mariana doesn't. She hates me and I hate her.'

Kate sighed. How could she help things? If Randel married Mariana it was terribly important that Rosa should not mind. How could she help Rosa to love Mariana? 'Darling, I think it's just that Mariana is not used to children,' she began, and saw how lame it was. Rosa had lived with Mariana and her grandmother all her life.

'Come and swim!' James's voice called loudly through the still air.

Obediently, Kate and Rosa ran down to the sea, going straight to his side.

James grinned at Kate. 'Are you never tired,

girl?'

She laughed, 'It's such heaven to be here.' She shook back her hair, her eyes bright. She met Randel's amused glance and said a little defiantly, 'You see, you forget I'm used to English weather—to me, this is out of this world.'

Mariana's voice was cool. 'You look very hot, Kate. I hope you won't be ill. Is this English climate so terrible that you all despise it so? It is strange indeed to me, how un-unpatriotic you are. England is your land, you should defend it.' Her voice was prim, smug.

Kate looked startled. 'Oh, we're always rude about our weather.'

Randel chuckled. 'Actually, Mariana, we British are so darned arrogant that we are proud of our shocking climate.'

Mariana stared at him. 'But that seems to me strange. You would die for your country—yet you insult it.'

The two men exchanged amused glances and then James winked at Kate.

'To the English, nothing is sacred. Climate —the railways—politics . . .' he said, half laughing. 'The English reserve the power and right to insult themselves.'

'How I long to see England,' Mariana said, her voice changing. 'It is odd that I have been to America—to Germany—but never to England.'

James was still laughing. 'You'd hate it,

Mariana. The men are stuffy and terrified of their wives—you'd be like a fish out of water.'

'A fish?' Mariana looked offended and bit her lip. 'Why is it right for Kate and not for me?'

'I can't see you in a yellow fog, Mariana, shivering—or when there is snow on the ground and the pipes freeze and the water has to be carried in pails, standing in the rain, queueing for a bus, fighting in the underground. No, it's all right for Kate. English girls are adaptable.'

'So!' Mariana was really angry now. 'I am not—how you call it?—the adaptable.'

Randel spoke for the first time. 'I don't agree, James. I think Mariana would fit in.' He looked at her thoughtfully. Kate was near enough to see the tender expression in his eyes. 'I can see Mariana making a wonderful entrance at the Opera . . . opening a bazaar and being given a bouquet of home-grown sweet peas by a small child.' He smiled. 'I would like to show you the Crown Jewels, Mariana—that would widen your enormous eyes. Take you to dinner, perhaps even to a royal garden party. I think you're right, Mariana, and you would love England.'

Kate had already turned away, feeling that Randel was talking to Mariana alone, for he had lowered his voice, his hand on her bare arm, a significance in his words. And Mariana was looking up at him, showing her lovely throat, her deep wondering eyes, her mouth parted eagerly.

'Rosa,' Kate said softly, 'why not give those shells to your father?'

Rosa's young eyes met hers thoughtfully and then the child smiled—a grave understanding smile. She went to her father and held out her hand.

'Look, Father,' she said said in her young clear voice. 'I have found you a present.'

It was as if only Rosa now existed. Kate saw the change on Randel's face. 'Why, Rose!' He dropped on one knee and took the shells almost reverently. 'They're beautiful—I'll always keep them.'

'Always?' Rosa asked solemnly.

He put his arm tentatively round her shoulders. Kate held her breath. She could imagine what was in his mind. This was Rosa's first attempt to reach him—he knew that and was afraid to spoil the moment.

'Al . . .' he began.

Mariana put in quickly, 'Really, Rosa, those are just stupid shells. Your father doesn't want to be laden with them.' She stopped as Randel turned his head and looked at her.

Kate let out her breath with a little sigh. Rosa's face had closed up again, Randel looked annoyed—and Mariana—for the moment—abashed, as if not sure what she had said wrong.

CHAPTER XII

Once they returned to Lourenço Marques, it seemed to Kate as if that idyllic interval on the yacht had never been. Life resumed its solid tempo and Kate rarely saw Randel Lister. Not that he was neglecting Rosa, for now he took her out on Sundays—but Mariana always went along, telling Kate with a malicious smile that she could 'have the day away.' It meant, of course, that Kate spent her Sundays with the McCormacks, something she normally enjoyed; yet the stress that Rosa obviously underwent each Sunday meant that Kate grew to dread the weekends. Not that Rosa had nightmares, but Monday morning would see her very quiet, find her eyes glancing quickly at Kate's face and away again, as if there were questions she longed to ask.

One day she asked Kate, 'If you have got to marry someone, Kate, why don't you marry my father?'

Kate was cutting out doll's clothes they were going to stitch together. She sat back on her heels and looked at Rosa. 'But, darling, I haven't got to marry anyone.'

Rosa looked solemn. 'Mariana says you are looking for a husband. If you are, Kate, please marry my father.' Her hands clutched Kate's arm and her face crumpled. 'I don't want

185

Mariana to be—'

Kate held her close, rocking her. What new mischief was Mariana up to? She told Rosa very gravely, 'There is only one man in all the world, Rosa, whom I would marry.' Her tone caught the child's attention. Rosa stopped crying and looked at her. 'Rosa—that man is your father.'

Kate was frightened by the sudden hope on Rosa's face, and blamed herself for raising it. 'Darling,' Kate went on quickly, 'your father doesn't want to marry me, so I can't. You see, you must love someone very much.'

It was hard to make Rosa understand what was meant by 'love.'

'You love my father?' she asked, frowning.

Kate sighed. 'Yes, I do,' she said bluntly.

'Then why doesn't he love you? If someone loves me, I love them.'

'But poppet,' Kate said, kissing her quickly, 'you're not a man. Men are different. Whoever your father loves, you will love too, because whoever it is, she is sure to love you.'

Kate saw by the stubborn look on Rosa's face that it was no good telling her that.

'Isn't Mariana much kinder to you now?' Kate went on. 'When you go out on Sundays, and—'

Rosa smiled. An old smile for one so young. 'Only when my father is there.'

Oh dear! Kate thought. And gave it up. If only she could find some way to help Rosa to

186

like Mariana—but Mariana seemed to do everything she could to antagonise the child. But what would happen when Mariana married Randel?

Kate was sure now that it was *when* and no longer *if.*

Mrs. McCormack agreed with her. 'That poor Mrs. Kelly—she's just out of hospital after a nervous breakdown,' she said. Kate had not told her about the meeting in the park, and decided it was too late to do so now. 'She is telling everyone that they are secretly engaged,' Mrs. McCormack continued.

'But why?'

Mrs. McCormack shrugged. 'She likes to imply that she has secret information. I'm sure Randel Lister would tell you, Kate. He'd want you to prepare Rosa.'

'I wish I knew how to do that,' Kate said bitterly.

Kate was visiting Natala regularly in hospital, and she was progressing well. One day Natala was allowed to walk.

Her face was radiant. 'Tomorrow I see my mother!' she exclaimed.

But unfortunately she did not, for Natala's mother died the next day. She had barely spoken since she went to hospital, and Natala had no chance, even, to see her at the end. James took complete charge, to Kate's great relief. He arranged for the funeral, saw the doctor because Natala had collapsed in hysterics, and then drove Kate back to the Pensio.

Outside, he parked his car and went with her to the door. He looked down at her.

'Kate, you mustn't suffer from other people's troubles.'

Her tear-stained face tried to brighten. 'I can't help it, James. I know how I'd feel if I lost my mother. It was terrible enough when my father died.'

'I know.' His hand was warm on hers. 'Dear Kate,' he said gently.

'Oh, James, if only my mother was here and we had a home. I can't bear to think of Natala going back to that dreadful room. Mother could have had her to stay with us.'

He smiled and got back into his car. Kate came to stand by the window, looking down at him.

'Kate,' he said. 'Mother and I have often talked about Natala—we knew this must happen. She is coming to stay with us.'

'James!' Kate was so happy she could hardly speak. Swiftly she bent and kissed him. 'Oh, James, you really are wonderful!'

She stood still, watching him wave and drive off. Then, as she turned, she saw Randel Lister on the pavement behind her, an odd look on his face. She wondered how long he had been standing there. She told him impulsively:

'Natala's mother has died and Natala is going to James's home. Isn't that wonderful

188

of them?'

He looked at her almost coldly. 'I think it's very good of them,' he said.

'Rosa is asleep, but she'll be waking up now,' Kate told him, deciding to ignore the cold tone. Maybe he had seen her kiss James and thought she was trying to find an excuse for it. 'Are you coming up to see her?'

'It was my intention,' he said with even greater coldness.

They went up the stairs in silence. Looking around, she wondered for the millionth time that he could not see how unsuitable this place was for a child to live in. What was it Mrs. McCormack had said once? 'None so blind as those that don't want to see.' Perhaps that was it.

The months were passing swiftly, the weather was already changing, with heavy winds, torrential showers, and Kate thought, with a sense of panic, of the moment that must come—the moment when they went back to England and she walked out of the Listers' lives. If only she knew what Randel Lister's plans were—if he still meant to send Rosa to boarding-school. Mariana would be the first to say that was a good idea!

Rosa was dressed and waiting in her room, carefully dressing her doll. She looked up and saw her father, and her face changed.

'We were going to the museum,' she said, hurrying to Kate's side, her face disappointed.

Randel's voice was stiff. His smile hid the pain that showed in his eyes.

'You can still go, Rosa. I just came to bring you—this.'

Awkwardly he held out a small parcel, Rosa took it, her eyes brightening. She sat on the floor to undo the parcel, taking a long time over it. Kate wondered what was in the child's mind. She kept her fingers crossed, praying that neither Rosa nor her father would be disappointed.

Rosa lifted a radiant face. The parcel contained a musical box—small, daintily carved. When she lifted the lid, tinkling music filled the air as it played *Oranges and lemons, said the bells of St. Clements.*

'How lovely!' Kate said eagerly.

Rosa hugged it, beaming at her father. 'Oh, thank you! Thank you!' she cried.

He looked embarrassed. 'I remembered you said she knew no nursery rhymes—I thought . . .'

'It's a wonderful present. Every time she plays it, she'll think of you,' Kate told him warmly.

His eyes met her quizzically. 'And not of James?' he said softly.

Kate tried not to look worried. 'It's just that she sees more of him,' she tried to explain, almost apologetically. 'He plays with her, teaches her to swim.'

'Not very surprising, really,' Randel Lister

said, and Kate looked at him quickly, for his voice sounded bitter, almost ironic. 'Seeing that you spend most of your time with James, it's natural that she should know him better than me.'

There was silence, broken only by the tinkling tune. Kate looked worriedly down at Rosa, but Rosa was engrossed in the music. Then Kate looked at Mr. Lister.

'I . . . do you object?' she said stiffly. It had sounded like a complaint—even a lecture.

Randel Lister shrugged. 'What right have I to mind? Your private life is your own. But are you sure you're wise? You're very young—it could be infatuation.'

Kate caught her breath. 'I'm not as young as *that,*' she said indignantly, 'and it certainly isn't infatuation that I feel for James.'

Kate stopped, for the front door had opened, the click-clack of high heels could be heard.

'Randel—ah, my Randel!' Mariana was calling. Now she stood there, breathless, delectably lovely in her tangerine-coloured silk frock with a small hat over one dark eyebrow, her hands outstretched. 'Oh—this is my good fortune day. I was feeling so sad—so alone. I telephoned you and you were out, my Randel. I come home in despair, and here—here you are.'

She stopped, aware of the music tinkling and Rosa's engrossed interest.

Mariana frowned. 'Randel, you foolish boy. Did you buy that expensive toy? It is absurd of you—she will break it. So much money!' she scolded.

Rosa looked up and promptly shut the lid of the box, cutting off the music abruptly. 'I won't break it,' she said, in the nearest approach to a rude voice Kate had ever heard her use. 'I won't break it!' Rosa said again, and her face crumpled.

Kate stooped. 'We know you won't, darling,' she comforted the child.

Mariana spread out her hands. 'You see, Randel—always it is as I say. She is getting beyond control, cheeky—and Kate allows it.'

'I don't . . .' Kate began, but Randel Lister took charge.

'If you're so unhappy, Mariana, I'd better cheer you up. Goodbye, Rose, Kate.' He was gone, down the passage, his hand on Mariana's arm.

Mariana's clear voice travelled. 'What were you talking to Kate about so seriously?'

Kate could not hear his answer. She wondered what Mariana would say if she knew that Randel had practically asked her if she was in love with James!

She managed a smile. 'I'll change my frock, Rosa, and then we'll go to the museum.'

They did not stay there long, for Kate felt emotionally exhausted and thought Rosa looked tired. That night, Rosa asked her to lock the musical box up in her suitcase. Without questioning the request, Kate obeyed, but it distressed her very much to see the extent of Rosa's fears as the days passed, for either Rosa carried the little music box with her wherever she went, or gave it to Kate for safe keeping.

A spell of wonderful weather came—warm but not too hot, ideal for the beach. Rosa and Kate acquired the habit of going early every day, taking a picnic lunch with them. James had presented Rosa with a gaily striped sun-umbrella which they could dig into the sand, and Rosa and Kate spent many happy hours under it, talking, listening to the tinkling of the beloved musical box, or just watching the sea shimmer and sparkle in the sunshine.

Kate had to ask the Pensio to pack picnic lunches for them, wishing—as she did so often—that they had a kitchen of their own, so that she could prepare Rosa's food. She still felt that Rosa should be having more vegetables and salad, although she tried to improve the child's diet by buying as much fruit as she could.

One morning, their lunch was particularly heavy—cardboard cartons of veal and some rich sauce, then fruit salad and coffee. The coffee, Kate thought, was exceptionally bitter, and both she and Rosa made little grimaces. Kate had often wondered if she could buy a small percolator and make their own—but there again, that was difficult, for there were no power plugs in the flat, and she was not sure how to work anything off the light.

Rosa and Kate curled up in a hollow in the sand, talking lazily. Kate was telling Rosa, once again, the fascinating story of Peter Pan. Rosa's favourite character in it was Tinkerbell, and Kate had taught her to use a small hand mirror to make the little flashing light.

They had the beach to themselves, only the sound of the sea and the casual call of a stray sea gull to break it. Kate was talking. And then, quite suddenly, she opened her eyes. She must have fallen asleep!

Rosa was not there.

Kate sat up, staring at the empty place by her side. She stood up, but the empty sands stretched away on either side.

It had to be a dream . . . but it was not. It was a nightmare. She ran down to the water's edge, heart in mouth, and then reassured herself. The tide was coming in—not going out. It stretched away for miles, just ankle depth. No one, not even a child, falling and frightening herself, could drown in that.

Kate shaded her eyes against the glaring sun. Had Rosa gone off hunting on the rocks? But there were no rocks on this part of the beach just yards and yards of creeping blue water, creeping too gently to knock a child off her feet.

Kate ran back to their picnic place. No sign

of the child, except for her musical box, tucked under a corner of the rug they had lain on.

Kate picked it up. Rosa would not have left it there, she thought.

Suddenly she was so afraid she could hardly breathe. She felt rooted to the spot, as if her limbs were made of iron. Fear gripped her throat and she could feel hysteria rising.

Rosa would never have gone willingly—

There were her small white sandals, her socks. She was only wearing her swim suit. If Rosa had wanted to walk she would have dressed. Rosa was a queer child at times, showing her Portuguese upbringing; believing that it was not 'done' to be seen walking in public 'undressed,' or 'naked' as Mariana would—

Kate closed her eyes. Mariana!

Relief flooded her. Mariana must have done this to frighten her—watched till she slept and then taken Rosa away, knowing how upset Kate would be.

She dressed swiftly, gathering up everything, hurrying back to the Pensio.

Mariana was there, her face cold.

'What is wrong?' she asked angrily. 'You have lost Rosa?' Her face was horrified, her voice rose. 'You must be mad—how could you *lose* her?'

It was a bad half-hour for Kate, having to admit she had gone to sleep on the beach, even worse when she heard Mariana telephone Randel, her voice bitter.

'I told you—she is unsuitable, that one. She sleeps . . . and the child goes. What do we do? Yes, she says she has searched the sands. She says . . .' Mariana sneered. 'I am telling you, my Randel, that she is not to be trusted. She sleeps . . .'

Kate turned away miserably. How could she have allowed herself to fall asleep? Such a thing had never happened before.

Randel's eyes were cold when he arrived to question her. 'I can't understand it!' he said.

She was nearly in tears. 'We're wasting time here—we must look for her,' she told him.

'I've phoned the police,' he informed her coldly. 'Now we'll go down to the beach. Surely she would not have left you?'

'I don't think she went willingly,' Kate said, and saw that he believed she was inventing a wild story to excuse herself. 'She left this—' she showed him the musical box. 'She always looked after it. When she did not keep it in her own hands, she made me lock it away,' she told him, not caring that Mariana stood there, her face hard. 'I telephoned James, but he's away,' she finished miserably.

Randel's mouth twisted bitterly. 'I think we can manage without his aid, just for once.'

The Senhora chose that moment to come in, standing monumentally in the hall, her heavy black clothes clinging, her jet beads swinging. When she heard the news, she had hysterics, moaning, accusing Kate of wicked neglect—of being *incompetanta.*

Kate and Randel went to the beach to search, but not even a footstep could they find.

'Not surprising—such fine sand shows nothing,' Randel said curtly.

It was all Kate could do not to cry. She stared at his hard, angry face and blamed herself bitterly. Yet surely he could see how worried she was—couldn't he understand what it meant to her?

As if he guessed what she was thinking, he looked down at her. 'Don't you start having hysterics too,' he said bluntly. 'Two hysterical women on my hands are bad enough.'

In the end they gave it up. The police had arrived, and Kate had shown them where they had eaten lunch. The police spread out a cordon—were talking of netting the sea. Someone mentioned sharks—and Kate went so white that Randel caught her by the arm to steady her.

'You can cut that thought right out,' he told her curtly. 'Rose wouldn't go out of her depth.'

Feeling better, Kate tried to smile. They walked back to the Pensio.

'Naturally the Senhora is distressed,' Randel said. 'She has loved and cared for Rose since she was a baby.' Then he had an idea. 'Rose may have gone to Mrs. McCormack,' he suggested.

Kate lifted a suddenly hopeful face. 'I never

thought of that. Mrs. McCormack was out when I telephoned, and the houseboy told me James was away.'

They went to the Villa Paradis. Mrs. McCormack was shocked. No, she said, she had not seen Rosa. Natala came limping out of the little office James had made for her. She was now in charge of some charity accounts of which he was the chairman.

'Oh, Kate . . . our poor Rosa!' Natala said, her ethereal-looking face, with its deep-set eyes, tragic.

Randel glanced at her quickly, and Kate saw that he was surprised he had not thought Natala was speaking sincerely. Then Natala went pale.

'Kate!' she said in a frightened voice. 'Have you thought Rosa might have been kidnapped?'

The ugly word hung in the air.

'Who would kidnap a child?' Randel began—but there was uncertainty in his voice.

Mrs. McCormack's eyes were troubled. 'It could be,' she said worriedly.

Kate was standing, tense and afraid. 'Oh, no—please, no!' she almost whispered. 'I couldn't bear her to be frightened again.'

She met Randel's questioning eyes.

'She was so afraid at first, but now . . . now she is beginning to trust people.' But not much, she thought unhappily. 'Anyway, who would kidnap her?' she went on.

Randel moved uneasily. 'Money—there are people . . .' He looked at his watch. 'Look, Kate, we'll go back to the Pensio and see if they have heard anything. Then I'll get on to the police again.'

'But, Randel,' Kate was completely unaware that she had called him by his Christian name, 'if you do that, they may . . . may . . .' Her voice faltered on the words. 'Shouldn't you go to your hotel and wait for them to telephone you? They'll ask for a ransom.'

He stared at her. 'It sounds very melodramatic,' he protested.

Mrs. McCormack nodded slowly. 'That's the usual routine. Oh, it can't . . .'

In the end, Kate went back to the Pensio alone. Randel drove back to his hotel. Mariana came into the hall, her face accusing.

'You have not found her,' she stated.

Kate shook her head. She was so tired and unhappy, she wanted to curl up and just die. How could she bear it if anything happened to Rosa—and all through her own carelessness?

She went down the passage, almost blindly, Mariana behind her, reviling her, accusing her of having slipped away to an assignation, of having neglected the *bébé*.

It was a relief to reach her own room—to slam the door rudely in Mariana's face—to fall on the bed, to cry heartbrokenly. Why, oh, why, had she fallen asleep? She never, never slept in the middle of the day—never indulged in a siesta. What could have made her sleep so heavily? Usually the lightest movement awoke her.

Yet Rosa had been able to wake up and walk away.

It must have been a heavy sleep—almost as if she was drugged. She sat up. Drugged? How bitter the coffee had been. Both had remarked on it. The coffee was never very nice, but today it had been almost undrinkable.

She stood up, brushing back the damp, heavy hair, fighting her sleepiness. Her limbs still felt heavy, her movements sluggish. She went quietly down the corridor, not sure what to do, who to tell—or what good it would be.

They would only accuse her of making up a story.

She chanced to look in the bathroom, and stared at what she saw.

The flat was still. Kate ventured into the room, and lifted the thermos flask that the coffee had been in. It had been washed thoroughly—it was even now filled with clean cold water.

What did it mean? Fear curled her heart up into a tight ball. It could only mean one thing. The Dominguez!

They—who never washed a cup, a glass, leaving everything to the Pensio servant, who came at regular intervals. Why was the flask washed and left there? The servant would have taken it down to the Pensio's kitchen. It could only mean one thing. Kate went back to her room, her legs unsteady. It could only mean one thing—but who would believe her?

CHAPTER XIII

That evening was like one long nightmare. Randel telephoned several times, and Mariana informed Kate that the Senhor Lister desired her to stay in the flat as the police might wish to question her! She herself was going to help the Senhor search.

Kate padded up and down the corridor between her room and the telephone restlessly, wishing with all her heart that James wasn't away. He would have been so comforting.

It was hot, with a heavy storm threatening. Kate had a bath and changed into her yellow shortie pyjamas and nylon dressing-gown. Passing Rosa's bedroom door, on the way back to her own room, she tried not to think of the child. Ever since she had felt sure the Dominguez were involved—and if not, why the hasty, guilty washing-up of the thermos?—she had not worried so much. They would not hurt her.

Suddenly she heard a cry—a moan. Her heart seemed to stand still. She opened the door. And stared.

201

Lying on Rosa's bed was Rosa herself, still in her sandy swimsuit, her face flushed, creased red from lying on the pillow.

Rosa turned restlessly and half woke.

Kate was on her knees by the child's side, holding her close, saying very gently, 'Turn over, honey, it's just a dream.' Obediently Rosa turned over, one hand up under her cheek. Kate drew a thin blanket up over her and stood staring down at her thoughtfully, beginning to understand.

If Rosa had drunk sufficiently of that drugged coffee, someone could have scooped her up in their arms and carried her back here without awakening her.

Kate went to the window and stared out blindly. Could Rosa have been here *all the time?* Kate began to tremble. Could anyone be so cruel—so heartless? She thought of Randel's white, stricken face—of the police scouring the town— of her own heartbreak.

She closed the door softly and went to the telephone. Her hand was still shaking as she dialled the number.

When she heard Randel's anxious voice she could not speak at first, but then she told him, 'Rosa is all right—she's here. In her room.'

His excited questions buzzed in her ear. All she could think of was that she must make him understand what had happened.

'She's covered with sand. I think she has been here all the time.' She paused while he

202

expressed relief. Had no one looked in her room?—why had she not awakened?

'I think she was drugged,' Kate said deliberately. 'I'm sure I was drugged—that was why I slept so heavily.' She paused.

Randel had obviously turned away from the telephone, she could hear him talking, but not his words. Then she heard Mariana's sceptical clear voice distinctly.

Desperately Kate went on. 'Please, Mr. Lister, bring a doctor with you. Rosa half woke, but I persuaded her to sleep again. I don't think she need ever know how frightened we were.' She waited while he demurred. Wouldn't a doctor alarm her? Wasn't it best to let her sleep until morning? Was that some of Mariana's doing? Kate wondered. By the morning the effects of the drug would have vanished. She answered stiffly, 'I think she *should* see a doctor.' She felt almost weak with relief when he unexpectedly capitulated. Maybe he had noticed that Mariana did not want to call one. Then she dismissed that thought as foolish—Randel would never doubt Mariana.

Kate listened to his instructions. 'Yes, I am serious, Mr. Lister. Rosa is not sleeping naturally. I'm sure she was drugged.' She hung up the receiver and turned away.

The Senhora was standing in the doorway of her bedroom, a voluminous grey wrapper enfolding her huge body, her eyes malevolent.

203

How much had she heard? Or understood? And if she had, what did it matter?

Passing her, Kate said, 'Rosa is well, Senhora. She is sleeping. The Senhor is coming at once, and we are not to disturb her.'

The elderly Portuguese woman looked at her with inscrutable eyes.

'She has been there—the whole time,' she said. It was not a question.

Kate looked at her. 'I think so,' she said.

Suddenly she could hardly bear to be near the Senhora. How could they do such a thing?

She hurried to her bedroom and dressed. When she came out, she went running down the corridor, for the Senhora was in Rosa's room. Rosa was crying bitterly and the Senhora was scolding her in a shrill voice.

'This nakedness . . . this bad behaviour!'

Most of what the Senhora said was in Portuguese, but Kate understood enough to see that the Senhora was in a violent temper, and determined to take it out of the child. Or?— or no! To upset her so much as to make the doctor think she was not *normal?* The frightening thoughts rushed through Kate's mind.

Now she pushed the elderly woman aside and scooped Rosa up in her arms. Glaring at the Senhora, Kate said, 'I told you Mr. Lister said we were not to disturb her.'

The Senhora advanced, shaking her finger in Kate's face and screaming at her, 'I am the *bébé*'s grandmother. What right have you . . . ?'

Randel and Mariana walked right into the little scene, with a short, dapper, bearded man behind them. Randel grasped the situation and soon had the Senhora out of the door—they could hear her having hysterics down the corridor and Mariana's voice trying to calm her. Randel's eyes were icy as he looked at Kate.

'I told you—'

Holding Rosa tightly, Kate glared back. 'I told the Senhora what you said, but—'

'Why didn't you stop her?'

'I had to get dressed, and when I came out she was in here, screaming.' Kate could feel Rosa's burning tears on her neck. Now Rosa's sobs became hiccoughs, slowly dying away.

The doctor waited patiently, a rather wry smile on his mouth. He was Portuguese, and Kate, looking at him, wondered what he thought of the situation. When Rosa was finally calm, the doctor gave her a quick examination. He looked under her eyelids, at her tongue, tried a few of her reactions, then looked up at Randel.

'Indubitably,' he said, with only the faintest of accents. 'I can even tell you the name of the drug.'

Randel spread out his hands helplessly. 'But why drug them both—and take the child? Why?'

The doctor lifted an admonishing finger. 'I

205

will give the child a sedative—in the morning all will be forgotten.' He looked at Kate, his eyes twinkling. 'She is a little sandy, eh, but doubtless you will bathe her.'

Kate clung to Rosa's hand. She was frightened. So it *was* true . . .'

'I think I'd like her to sleep with me,' she said.

The doctor nodded. 'It is wise. Then she will be secure.' He turned to Randel, but Randel was frowning at Kate.

'Look, Kate, don't over-exaggerate this,' he said curtly. 'Our main idea is not to frighten Rose.'

Kate looked at him and wondered if he could see in her eyes the scorn she felt for him at that moment. 'The damage has already been done,' she said, and could not resist adding, 'by the Senhora.'

Kate found that the story of the abduction and discovery of Rose Lister was soon all over Lourenço Marques. She took Rosa to tea the following day with the McCormacks, and James's mother soon gave Rosa something to occupy her so that she and Kate could talk. Mrs. McCormack had met Mrs. Kelly in town. 'And, Kate, even though you dislike her, you would be sorry for her now. She said that I must warn you again. Kate, why *again?*'

Kate told of that first meeting. 'She really frightened me. She says the Dominguez are dangerous women and intend to hurt me.'

'He thinks *he* was lucky they came to *his* aid,' Kate said.

Natala shrugged. 'It may be so—they help each other. But now—what lies ahead? Mr. Lister, he takes the *bébé* to England. No more money. How the Dominguez live? That is what they ask. Mariana must marry. But why does the Senhor hesitate? She think it is you.' Natala smiled as Kate shook her head vigorously. 'That he likes and respects you, *Kett*, I am sure. I have seen with what eyes he stares at you. I agree—it is not love,' she went on, quite as if she did not realise how it hurt, but now Natala's eyes became kind and comforting. 'You know that, *Kett*, you are no fool. But Mariana sees you as enemy. One to be disposed of.' It was an ugly, body-shivering remark. 'So she tried to . . . to . . . delusion . . . to disillusion . . . to reveal . . .' She sighed. 'The word will not come. She try to make the Senhor think you bad at job—then he sack you and she look after Rosa again, plenty of money to live well and all are happy.'

They talked for hours in the same strain, and when Kate took Rosa back to the Pensio, both of them by their slow dragging walk displaying their reluctance, her heart was really heavy. In the next few days, Natala's words stayed with her. It seemed as if she was endangering Rosa just by staying with her.

Then the storm broke. It was learned that Antonio Vidal had been arrested—he had

208

been seen carrying the child into the Pensio. He was in the hands of the police. Mariana said it must be revenge—because Kate insulted him! Kate said she had not.

Natala wept bitterly. James tried to comfort her. 'It is all Mariana,' Natala sobbed.

James looked at Kate, and lifted his eyebrows. Later she told him that she thought Natala was right.

'But why?' James asked.

When she explained and told him of the drugged coffee, he wanted to know if she had told Randel.

'It was a strange thing for them to wash up that thermos. Yet why drug you?'

'I think I should go away,' Kate said unhappily. 'If I told Randel he wouldn't believe me.'

'No,' James agreed. 'He is bewitched. I wish we *could* open his eyes.'

It was then that he invited them all to go to a bullfight. He had first taken them all out to dinner at the Polano. It was an uncomfortable meal, and when Randel had danced with Kate, he lectured her on her attitude towards Rose.

'I understand she never leaves your side now. She sleeps with you—that you fight every attempt the Dominguez make to talk to her,' he said coldly.

Kate lifted defiant eyes. Oh, what was this awful emotion she felt for this man? It could not be love, surely? Even while she trembled at his touch, she could still shake with anger at his obtuseness, his refusal to see the truth.

'Rosa is terrified of them—the Senhora told her she had been kidnapped and that it was lucky she was found!' Kate's voice quavered before the anger in Randel Lister's eyes.

'Rose has great imagination,' he said cuttingly. 'Can't you see you are encouraging her? She *must* accept the Dominguez. She has known them all her life. They are her only relations—they love her. Your attitude makes everything very difficult.'

Seething with anger, yet miserably aware that every word he said proved that he planned to marry Mariana, Kate went back with him to the table. Mariana was being very gay—carefully ignoring Kate, addressing her remarks simply to the two men.

'Is it not wonderful, my Randel? James is taking us to see the great Costa de Merico,' she said almost reverently. 'He has the tickets.'

James turned to Kate. 'Would you care to come?' He smiled at her shocked face. 'Bullfights are not the same here as in Spain. Here the bull is not killed, he only fights once and then goes back to the fields to graze and enjoy life. They don't injure him—just tease him to make him angry. It's so colourful.'

Mariana spoke before Kate could answer. 'The Engleese mees would be sick. She has not the stomach for the fight. She would be afraid—cry.' Her voice was contemptuous.

'She could not see it as we do. Beautiful—a pageant—a trial of man's skill and courage.'

Kate was still going to refuse, but Randel surprised her by saying, with maddening smugness, 'Mariana is right, Kate. You would hate it.'

Kate took a deep breath. 'I think James is right and I ought to see it, as part of my education. I may never have such a chance again,' she said a little bitterly, and then regretted the words. She knew she would loathe every minute of it.

She was to regret her words still more on the day itself. It was a scorchingly hot day with the sky almost colourless because of the heat. Even the palm trees seemed to have lost heart, their leaves hanging listlessly. Rosa had been left with Mrs. McCormack. James kept close to Kate—for which she was grateful, especially as Randel had eyes only for the exquisitely lovely, elegantly dressed Mariana.

Mariana was in her element, waving to friends, bowing, looking very proud. Her excitement grew as she leaned forward and looked down into the ring.

The whole arena was packed with shouting, laughing, excited people. There was no shade and Kate's face began to burn and her eyes to ache. Inside her she felt sick with fear. Everyone—except Kate—seemed a little drunk.

'It's excitement,' James whispered when she

mentioned this. 'Look!'

He pointed out the brilliant blue velvet cloak, decorated lavishly with gold embroidery, its spangles sparkling in the sunshine, which had been thrown over the parapet before the day's guest of honour—a visiting film star, who sat a little stiffly, smiling determinedly at everyone who looked at her.

James showed Kate the sturdily-built wooden screens.

'The matadors jump behind them if the bull comes too close,' he explained.

Music started—gay, martial music. The picadors rode into the arena on great white horses, who looked as proud as their riders. Behind them marched the bandoleiros, strutting like peacocks in their skin-tight trousers and short gay jackets as they swung their hips and gazed round haughtily at the adoring shouts from the crowd. Then a pause and a sudden roaring cry as the matador entered the ring. He walked along, his cape swaying, his face beaming, as he bowed right and left.

Mariana turned, her face radiant. 'He is superb!' she said breathlessly.

Kate stared at him. An ordinary, rather plump, little man with a kind face—what was there so wonderful about him?

Everyone else thought there was, apparently. Roses and flowers were being tossed into the ring. Everyone was shouting.

For a second, Kate caught the infection of excitement.

But only for a short time. And then everything went wrong. The colour and gaiety was wiped out. The eager excited faces were distorted; now they were cruel, sadistic. She thought it was how the Romans must have looked when they watched the Christians being thrown to the lions.

It was all the bull's fault. Maybe if it hadn't been that bull—

He came into the ring so happily, so confidently. He looked round—every man was his friend. He was a great broad beast and he strolled nonchalantly, turning his head slowly from side to side, graceful, contented—with a dignity of his own.

And suddenly he lost his dignity, and his contentment.

Two picadors rode round the ring. They chased the bull. They harried him. He went from one side of the ring to the other, bewildered, surprised—obviously wondering what was happening.

It got worse. They made him run. Soon he was breathless, pawing at the ground, turning his head angrily, looking . . . a fool, Kate thought, as her eyes filled with sympathetic tears. She tried not to look, but the excited cries from the crowd made her imagine even worse things. James had said they would not hurt the bull.

Now the bandoleiros were walking round him, teasing him, flicking the cape in his face, then standing out of the way. Then the matador, as the bull rushed past, flicked something else—Kate saw a ribbon fluttering from the bull's neck—a pretty red ribbon.

And she saw the blood trickling down from the small wound.

'*Olé! Olé!*' everyone screamed excitedly.

The bull pawed the ground, looking round wildly. And another bandoleiro came—and another—and another—until the bull was plunging about, his neck half hidden by the ribbons, the blood trickling.

Kate knew she was going to be sick.

She put out her hand blindly and felt James take it.

It was like a nightmare; Kate was only conscious of James's arm round her as they pushed their way through the crowd, Kate fighting the nausea, stumbling over people. All she could hear was a wild frenzied shouting from the crowd:

'*Olé! Olé! Olé!*'

Somehow she found herself in a cloakroom, being sick, then washing her face and hands, trying not to hear the excited screams, not to picture . . .

James was apologetic as he drove her back to his house. 'I ought to have known,' he kept saying. 'I just wanted Randel to see . . .'

He never finished the sentence, for a car

rushed round the corner on the wrong side of the road and James was too busy slamming on brakes, righting his car out of a skid, to talk.

James told his mother that Kate should go to bed. 'I'll explain to the others,' he promised. 'Her nerves are shot to pieces.'

Kate saw the understanding look that passed between him and his mother.

'Kate and Rosa must spend the night here,' Mrs. McCormack said firmly.

Kate was thankful to lie between the cool sheets, to close her eyes, to try to forget the look on the bull's face. Cruelty of any sort always distressed her.

Natala could not understand her. 'To us—it is a chance for a man to show how brave he is,' she tried to explain.

'But if you could have seen the poor bull's face—'

Natala shook her head. 'The bull—he has no heart, no feelings.'

It was useless, Kate saw. They just thought of it from a different angle. Mrs. McCormack told her that James had returned to the bullfight. That several picadors were injured, but not seriously.

'I gather,' she finished dryly, 'that Mariana enjoyed herself.'

'She must have been very triumphant about me,' Kate said miserably. 'She said I had no stomach for a fight.'

'I should hope not, dear,' James's mother

215

said warmly. 'I wouldn't go to one.' She smiled at Kate.

'I don't think it's brave for all those men to attack one bull,' Kate said.

'Darling, neither do I, but—different countries, different ways. I think James was shocked by Mariana's intense excitement. On the other hand, Kate, we have our foxhunting —our stag-hunts. Yet we don't call that cruel.'

'I do,' Kate said stubbornly.

In the morning, Mrs. McCormack telephoned Randel Lister. Kate was in the room, a little surprised at Mrs. McCormack's rather dictatorial tone. It worked, though, and Mrs. McCormack discovered that the Senhora Dominguez had not passed on her message that Kate and Rosa would sleep at the Villa Paradis.

'I'm worried about Kate,' Mrs. McCormack said bluntly to Randel. 'She suffered a lot when Rosa disappeared. She is on edge— that's why she can hardly bear to let the child out of her sight. It's not good for either of them. This—this bullfight has just tipped the scales. My doctor is seriously concerned—' She smiled at Kate. It was a white lie! 'I am leaving tomorrow to stay in my cottage at Pumgeni,' she went on. 'I wondered if you would permit Kate and Rosa to come with me for a few weeks. It is an ideal setting, right on the beach, plenty of shade, and a safe paddling pool for Rosa.'

In the end, after a very short discussion, Mrs. McCormack turned triumphantly to Kate as she replaced the telephone receiver.

'He seemed quite relieved,' she said, her eyes twinkling.

Kate sighed. 'I expect he is. Now he can have Mariana without any encumbrances.' She turned her head away, for her eyes were filling with stupid tears.

She was wondering how she could bear to be two hundred miles away from him. Yet she should start getting used to that—for soon it might be six thousand miles!

CHAPTER XIV

The McCormacks' cottage was beautiful, hidden from the road by weeping willows and tall graceful palms, while down the windy side loomed dark cypresses, looking statuesque against the brilliantly light sky, where you could sit on the wide terrace, gazing over velvet-smooth lawns which ran right down to the white sand which was lapped by the blue waters of the Indian Ocean.

It was not a cottage in the sense that Kate would have used the word, for it had large gracious rooms and so many servants that she lost count. It was sheer luxury to be there after the dingy, frightening atmosphere of the

Pensao Fadora.

Rosa obviously loved the cottage too. She seemed immediately relaxed, almost as though she also felt safe. There was a plump African girl called Beauty who took charge of Rosa, and Rosa liked her from the beginning.

'I thought you needed a real rest, Kate dear,' Mrs. McCormack said, a little apologetically, as she saw the look on Kate's face as Rosa went off, quite happily, for a walk with Beauty. 'And Rosa should get used to other people.'

Kate smiled at her. 'You're so right. I've been thinking that for some time. It was just— just that there was no one I could trust. I can't help feeling that if Randel does marry Mariana, they will come back here to live. I don't, for one moment, think that Rosa will ever become what he calls an English child. And if that happens, Rosa must get used to trusting people.' She sighed. 'You know, I'm not even sure that Randel wants Rosa to be an English child now.'

'He's a strange man,' Mrs. McCormack said.

'Strange, indeed,' Kate agreed, and closed her eyes quickly, hoping Mrs. McCormack could not read her unhappy thoughts.

After two weeks of lazing, 'not lifting a finger to do anything,' as Kate put it, with good food, plenty of sleep, and this lovely serene atmosphere, Kate felt a different girl. She had lost the tension, the nervous 'looking

218

over her shoulder' habit that worried James so much, even the quick aggressive protective movements she had made instinctively towards Rosa if anyone spoke to her. Now she could almost laugh at her fears about the Dominguez.

James drove Natala down to the cottage for a long weekend. Natala, also, was a new person. Her eyes followed James about, like, according to Mrs. McCormack's description, an adoring spaniel's. To Natala, James was a god. Not that Kate was surprised, especially when she heard Natala's latest news.

'He sends me to America! There is the latest treatment. He says I may even be a complete *cure*,' Natala said in an awed whisper. 'He is so good, so kind. He even tries to help Antonio.'

James told them about that later. Looking at Kate, he said, 'You were quite right. It *was* Mariana's fine hand behind that abduction of Rosa.' He looked grim. 'Vidal was a mass of frightened jelly—they don't treat their prisoners as V.I.P.'s in Mozambique, you know—and I easily got the truth out of him. Mariana promised him no one would know— that it was *the joke*!'

'But why should she do such a thing? How could she be so cruel?' Kate asked.

James shrugged. 'I suppose she didn't see it as cruel. She has no idea of what it means to love a child—to worry so desperately about its being frightened. I guess she wanted Lister to think you were not capable of looking after Rosa.' He smiled ruefully. 'Funny—I dropped some pretty broad hints to Lister as to who was behind the plot, and for one moment I thought he was going to hit me. I've never seen him so angry. Anyhow, I managed to persuade him that Vidal had been badly scared, that Rosa was not hurt, nor even frightened, that it had been done as a peculiar idea of humour. Then Lister contradicted me. He said that Vidal had done it solely out of revenge because of the way he had been treated by you, Kate. That you encouraged him and then snubbed him.' Before Kate could speak, James lifted a hand. 'Don't say it, Kate, we all know that's a lie. It was Mariana's story, of course. What a woman!'

'James,' Kate ventured to say, 'I always thought you were in love with her.'

James's head shot up in surprise as he stared at her. 'Me? In love with her? Heavens, no. She may be attractive, amusing—even astounding. But to be in love with her! Are you mad, Kate?' He stared at her so strangely that she felt quite uncomfortable. Then she realised the silence in the room and that both Natala and Mrs. McCormack were gazing at her.

'So what happened to Antonio?' Mrs. McCormack said hastily, almost as if she wanted to save the situation. But why? What situation was there?

Natala beamed. 'Ah—that you should ask! It is so wonderful.' She beamed at James, worshipping him, as his mother would have said. James looked sheepish and then winked at Kate.

'Look, isn't life ironical? If you want a girl to think you're wonderful, do something for the man she loves—the joke being, of course, that it doesn't benefit you at all.' He told them that Vidal was working for him. 'I think he'll turn out all right. He got in with a bad crowd, drinking, gambling, and also fell under Mariana's spell. I think he's a bit disillusioned about her.'

'Oh, he is,' Natala said happily. 'But tell them the rest of it.'

'Antonio is escorting Natala to America for me. He will act as my agent and also put through some quite important deals. I think he needs responsibility. I'll give it to him. I'm also giving him some introductions. We think they—I mean *he*—' James gave Natala a conspiratorial wink. '—may settle out there.'

'It would be so wonderful!' Natala said, her face glowing.

Just before James took Natala back to Lourenço Marques, Natala had a letter from a friend. She took it excitedly to the terrace to read it to them all. She was triumphant.

'I have been making the enquiry about the Dominguez,' she told them. 'This, then, is what I have heard. It says the same as the story I heard before, but this, now, is the certain truth. These people were in Lourenço Marques at the time they remembered the talk, the questions, the thoughts. Listen, if you please.'

James met Kate's eyes with an amused smile, but they settled down obediently while Natala installed herself on a straight chair before them, looking grave as a judge.

She told them that no one knew where the Dominguez came from originally. One moment they were not there—and then they were.

She began to giggle. 'We say maybe they come on the magic rug.'

'More likely broomsticks,' James suggested.

Natala ignored the remark. 'No one hears of them and then, hey presto, there they were. Accepted by Senhor Lister, settled in a *ménage,* looking after his child. It was queer. People talked, gossiped, wondered, then shrugged their shoulders and thought the obvious.'

Natala's cheeks turned a dull red for a moment as she looked hastily at James's mother. But Mrs. McCormack was only looking puzzled.

'They must have been his in-laws, though, if Mr. Lister gave them the baby.'

It was Kate's turn. 'He told me he had no idea that his wife had any relations at all. He thought she must have run away from home. Maybe there was an arranged marriage that was distasteful, he said.' Natala nodded and Kate went on, 'Or just that she wanted to see the world and her family didn't like it. Anyhow she never mentioned them, and he was sure she was an orphan. It was only when he was so desperate after losing his wife and wondering what to do with the baby that his in-laws miraculously turned up.

'He must have been very glad to see them,' Mrs. McCormack remarked.

'Oh, he was,' Kate said earnestly. 'He sounded as though he was desperate at the time. He loved Candida so very much, and then to lose her, and have a baby to care for. He has no relatives. His parents are dead. He never hears from his brothers, they have all drifted apart. He said it was wonderful when the Senhora and Mariana arrived, though he had a terrible time with them, for they were hysterical with grief. They said that they had heard she was very ill, dying, and had come at once. He thought it rather odd that he had not known anything about them, so he was sure that Candida had quarrelled with them—and that now it was too late they had forgiven her. He never liked to ask about the quarrel—they were too unhappy.'

Natala lowered her voice. 'My friend says that all are afraid of them—the Dominguez. No one dare make trouble lest a spell be cast.'

She saw James's sceptical smile and shook her finger at him. 'I am telling you—it is not all moonshine, Senhor James. Things have happened. That, I am sure, was why Antonio stole the *bébé*. He is not a bad man, that one. Just a little weak,' she said tenderly, as if it was a virtue. 'I know that he fears the Senhora greatly.'

Kate shivered. 'So do I. I don't blame him. I dread the thought of going back there.'

James looked at her. 'You don't need to think about that for a long time, Kate. I gather Lister is only too happy for you to be here with us.'

Natala was turning the letter over in her hand. She looked up, eyes bright, still hesitating. 'I know not if to tell you this. If they guessed . . .' She shivered. It seemed to Kate that everyone shivered when they talked of the Dominguez, so it was not only her imagination that cloaked them with such melodramatic garb. She saw that Natala, while nervous, was longing to tell them.

'They say . . . that it is believed that the Senhora and Mariana were not related to the Senhor Lister's wife at all.'

The startling words fell into the room, leaving a long silence.

'But Mariana is Candida's sister,' Kate said.

'Mariana says so. Can she prove it?' Natala asked, shrugging her shoulders.

James was frowning. 'That's quite an

224

accusation, Natala. Are you implying that they have succeeded in deceiving Lister for all these years? I'm sure he would have demanded proof before handing over the baby.'

'I wonder,' Mrs. McCormack said, at once. 'Picture yourself in such a situation, James. Your wife has died, you are stranded with a sick, helpless baby, your employers expect you to carry on with your job and not allow your personal problems to take precedence. You know what big firms are like.' Her voice was crisp. 'Randel must have been desperate. A home or foster parents for his child? Then, out of the blue, along come his wife's heartbroken mother and sister. How could he ask them for proof?'

'You must think, Senhor James,' Natala said in a demure voice, her eyes wide. 'When you have a Mariana who cries and clings to you, for she is heartbroken, can you then ask for birth certificates?'

It wasn't very funny, but Natala's voice and expression made them all collapse with laughter. Perhaps it was as well, Kate thought, for she had been tensed up, before, with anger for Randel's having been so deceived.

Mrs. McCormack was obviously thinking it all out. 'But—but what did the Dominguez get out of it? I mean, that dreadful Pensio . . .'

James and Natala stared at her as if she was mad. 'Mother—all these years, Randel has kept both these women. Paid their expenses,

225

paid for all sorts of extras, for, knowing him, I know he would never query them. The Senhora is at ease in a place like that. I'm sure many of Mariana's trips away have been paid for by Randel—they would say it was doctors' bills or clothes. He would never query it. Besides, it gave them a hold on him—he has had to feel all this time under an obligation. If it's true—then the Dominguez have done very well out of their deception.'

'Do you think it can be true, James?' Kate asked.

He frowned. 'It could, you know. It would explain many things. Kate—' His voice changed, became hard, almost authoritative. 'Promise you won't go back to the Pensio without letting me know. I may be away, and . . .'

She stared at him. 'James—do you think I might be in danger?'

'You could be. I don't like the set-up, Kate. You see, you're the stumbling block in their continuation of this good life. If you weren't there . . .' He sighed. 'I wonder how we could find out? It's no good telling Lister what we think. I'd probably get a black eye for my pains. How blind can a man be?'

James and Natala left for Lourenço Marques the next day. Kate kissed the Portuguese girl warmly and wished her all the luck in the world.

Natala's eyes were glowing. 'Even if I do not

get the cure,' she said, 'I will have the happiness. Antonio will be there, and I think . . .' She closed her eyes and her hand went to her heart, in a funny poignant little gesture Kate had seen her make once before. 'I pray—my dear *Kett*—I pray.'

After they had gone, Kate found herself thinking about James. Had there ever been anyone like him? He was wonderful—no doubt about it, wonderful. Yet such good fun, too.

A week passed, and Mrs. McCormack had a long letter from James. She took it to Kate, who was lying in a hammock under a palm tree, apologising as usual for her laziness.

'I'll never be able to work again,' Kate said.

Mrs. McCormack looked at her. 'Perhaps you won't have to,' she said. Then the plump affectionate face looked startled and dismayed, almost as though she wished she could unsay the words. She went on hurriedly, 'James has told me to tell you what's in the letter. I'll read it to you—at least, some of it.'

James had been with Randel Lister.

' "He came to see me, he was half furious, half amused," he wrote. "I was surprised at his coming to me, for I'm sure he didn't want a solution to his problem, just reassurance that he was right. He's certainly got an uncomfortable conscience. It seems some ancient relative of Mariana's called on Lister—seedy sort of man, very correctly

227

dressed and wearing a monocle he was not used to—he said he was her uncle. Before Lister knew what was happening this individual was asking Lister what were his 'intentions' and were they honourable? He was aggressive and said it was time the marriage was arranged."'

Mrs. McCormack stopped reading and stared at Kate. 'Well, I am surprised!'

Kate nodded. 'I'd have thought Mariana would be more subtle—it isn't like her. Besides, she doesn't need to use a shotgun to get him to marry her.'

Mrs. McCormack gave her a quick, shrewd glance. 'I'm not so sure, dear. Now I'll go on. James says: "Lister asked the uncle for the reason of the visit—why the sudden interest in Mariana's affairs. The uncle said that Mariana was being 'talked about'—that in a small place, her reputation should be guarded. I gather Lister broke out into almost hilarious laughter at this—and told the uncle that Mariana's sole aim in life was to be talked about. But not in that way, the uncle said, becoming very pompous. Anyhow, to cut a long if amusing story short, they parted in anger, the uncle threatening a court case. He told Lister that Mariana had refused many good offers of marriage because she had to look after the child. That she had said she owed her first duty to the child and would not consider her own happiness. Lister repeated this to me and it was all I could do not to laugh. I found that it was this bit that worried him. He asked me if I thought it was true. I said, No. If anything, it improved Mariana's chances of making a good marriage, for it gave a cloak, albeit rather thin, of respectability and let people see that underneath that hard, shining exterior there might be some heart."' Mrs. McCormack lowered the letter and stared at Kate. 'James said some dreadful things.'

Kate nodded again. Dear James! 'I suppose Randel was angry at that?' she asked.

Mrs. McCormack returned to her letter. 'James says, "Lister then told me of the terrible scene he had had with Mariana. She descended on him and wept in his arms, apologising for her wicked old uncle, saying she had not known of his visit, that the uncle was a mercenary and that she understood Randel's difficult position. She said she was happy to go through life alone, solitary, unloved, but she had cared for his *bébé*. That made life worth living. I gather this was what was really worrying Lister. As I said before, he has a conscience that has an uncomfortable habit of rearing its ugly head now and then. He is not sure if he has wickedly made use of Mariana, or if she is trying to force his hand. She told him she knew he did not love her, but she was content to have it that way. Just to care for his child was satisfaction enough."' Mrs. McCormack stopped reading.

229

'Poor Randel,' she said warmly. 'How embarrassing for him!'

When Kate did not answer, James's mother read on: ' "As you see, a very emotional and happy evening was spent by Mariana. It took me hours to calm Randel down, sort out his conscience, show him how the Dominguez had also benefited by the arrangement—very much so. He couldn't see that. Mariana had given up her life, he said. How, I asked, and reminded him of her journeys overseas, the gay life she led. In the end I suggested, if he was really conscience-stricken, that he give her a settlement—a lump sum. It would do for a dowry, or buy her a new wardrobe and she could go off to pastures new. He didn't like that very much." ' Mrs. McCormack paused again.

'I'm sure he didn't,' Kate said softly. Poor Randel—why didn't he make up his mind? It was obvious he loved Mariana. What made him hesitate?

Mrs. McCormack said slowly, 'I've left the worst bit until the end, Kate. James is bringing them down for a long weekend.'

'Oh, no!' Kate cried in dismay.

'I'm afraid so. I wonder why. James is usually more thoughtful,' his mother said worriedly. 'We're so happy here, just the three of us.'

Kate tried to smile, but her face felt stiff. How could she bear it, to be near Mariana—to feel her flesh creep, to have that old senseless feeling of fear? Irrational fear, James had said once. But was it when you knew a person hated you so much? Was it irrational then? And if Natala's astounding story was true, and the Dominguez were frauds, then how much more reason had Mariana to hurt her? Then she remembered James. He would be there—so Mariana would not be able to harm her.

She stood up. 'Maybe it won't be so bad,' she said to Mrs. McCormack. 'Can I help you plan menus and things so that you can enjoy yourself while they're here?'

'Enjoy myself?' James's mother asked. 'I won't have a moment's happiness until that woman is out of my house. I can't think why James should ask her.'

As it turned out, it was not so bad—at first. Mariana was at her most charming, on her best behaviour; kind but distant to the cautious Rosa who kept out of her way as much as she could; pleasantly friendly, if slightly chilly, to Kate; very polite and respectful to Mrs. McCormack and completely enchanting to the two men, playing them off against one another, with a gracious, attractive air, so that neither need be jealous, yet each man was made to feel sure he was the favoured one. It was a clever game, rather amusing to watch. Or it might have been had Kate not felt so desperately unhappy. Just to be so near Randel, to have him gaze at Mariana like that—to laugh at her jokes, to hold her close as they danced—how could Kate be anything but miserable?

The first day passed pleasantly, with sunbathing, Kate and James swimming in the pool, and all of them dancing in the evening on the terrace. The second day, James took Rosa and Kate for a walk along the sand dunes. There was a slight breeze and Kate had to hold on to her big floppy cotton hat. She was surprised because James had tried to get out of taking Rosa with them, the first time he had ever done such a thing. Now Rosa ran ahead to pick up a gay feather that had floated down and Kate looked up into James's smiling face and said impulsively: 'Oh, James, it's so wonderful here. I could live here for ever!'

To her surprise, he grabbed her hand and held it tightly and his face seemed to change, grow to look almost desperate. 'Why don't you, Kate? We could live here half of the year. You know I love you.'

He stopped speaking and dropped her hand. She knew her face had told him what she thought he already knew.

'Oh, James,' she said, and thought how inadequate it sounded. 'Oh, James,' she repeated in dismay. She wanted to cry. 'I like you so much, but—'

He turned his head away for a moment. She wondered what one did in such a situation. What good were words?

232

'I ought to have known,' said James. 'I suppose in my heart, I've always known, and yet I went on hoping. It's Lister.'

'It always has been, James,' she said unhappily. 'Right from the first time I saw him.'

He turned and was himself again—kind, friendly, even protective.

'Don't fash yourself, Kate,' he said gently. She wanted to cry more than ever. 'It's just one of those things. I'll get over it.'

She could not help herself, she caught hold of his arm and leaned against him, trying to show her sorrow, her sympathy.

'I wish—oh, how I wish . . .' She paused. 'James, you've been so good to me. I'm so happy with you. I love your mother—'

He patted her hand gently. 'I know, dear.'

Rosa was tugging at Kate's hand. Both had forgotten the child. Now she looked up at them, her face anxious. 'Has Kate hurt herself?' she asked.

Kate shook her head. Her eyes were enormous with unshed tears. 'I've hurt Uncle James and I can never forgive myself,' she told the child.

'Don't say that, Kate,' James began.

Rosa looked at him. 'Where does it hurt?' she asked. 'I could kiss it if you like.'

James knelt by her side and lifted his face, touching his mouth.

'It hurts here,' he said. Rosa kissed him

233

gently, and James smiled. 'It's much better now. Nearly well,' he told her.

'I'm glad,' Rosa said, and tucked her hand in his.

They walked back in silence, Kate still struggling with tears. It was awful to have had to hurt him—James, of all people.

It was even worse when they got back and she saw the quick hopeful way Mrs. McCormack looked at them. Had she guessed James was going to propose? Kate's heart sank when she saw the disappointment on the older woman's face and the quick way she tried to hide it.

Kate escaped to her bedroom, with Rosa close behind, and stood by the window, her hands over her eyes.

'Why did you hurt Uncle James?' Rosa asked.

'Yes, why?' a cold voice asked.

Kate swung round, startled. It was Mariana. She had followed them through the open door and stood there. Her white pleated frock clung to every curve of her body, and as she moved forward Kate saw the angry hate in her dark eyes.

'Tell me,' Mariana insisted. 'Why did you hurt Uncle James?' Cruelly she mimicked Rosa's voice.

Rosa turned. 'He wants to marry Kate,' she said defiantly. 'But Kate will only marry my father.'

Kate caught her breath with dismay. Mariana's face lost its coldness, became distorted with hideous anger.

'So that is it!' She came into the room, closing the door softly, crossing swiftly to Kate's side. 'You little—' She called Kate some name in Portuguese. It sounded ugly. Then her hand flew out, hitting Kate's cheek viciously, leaving a deep red mark on the pale skin. 'You leave him alone. Do you hear me? Or you'll get more than a slap on the face . . .' Mariana's voice was shaking. 'He's mine! Mine! *Mine!*' she screamed at Kate. Then she seemed to remember something.

'James too? I wondered why he . . . Oh, you are the one, again!'

Mariana's hand flew out again, giving another vicious crack as she hit Kate. Kate rocked back on her heels. She seemed unable to think, to do anything. She put her hand to her face—and felt Rosa clutching her, shouting angrily, 'Get out! Get out!'

And then Mariana had gone. The room was very quiet. The door was closed. And Rosa was comforting her, holding Kate close, kissing the stinging red cheek, saying over and over again that she loved Kate and hated Mariana.

Kate wondered what to do. It would be difficult to face the others as if nothing had happened. She looked ruefully at her cheek. Even thick make-up could not hide the marks. In the end, she and Rosa had a 'secret.' Kate pretended to have a headache and Rosa asked Mrs. McCormack if they could both have dinner in bed.

Rosa touched the sore cheek tenderly. 'Does it still hurt?' she asked.

Kate shook her head, and begged Rosa not to tell anyone. It was bad enough to have made Uncle James unhappy—Kate did not want to make Rosa's father sad too.

'He would be cross,' Rosa said solemnly. 'He says it is bad to lose your temper and hit people.'

Kate agreed—but wondered a little bitterly with whom Randel would be cross. With herself, she was sure. He would be vexed and embarrassed to know that Rosa was telling people that her nursery-governess was in love with him.

Fortunately by the morning the marks had almost vanished, so Rosa and Kate could go in to breakfast. James looked up from serving the kidneys and bacon, and smiled. 'Headache better, Kate?' he asked, and his kind eyes told her that he thought she had kept away out of consideration for him.

Mariana, coming in to breakfast for once, spoke politely, but her eyes might have been made of glass. Kate wondered if it was imagination, but she seemed to feel vibrations of hate flowing out of Mariana's body—it made it hard to eat, to talk normally. Rosa walked deliberately round the table to avoid passing Mariana. Kate saw that Randel perceived this and was half frowning, half amused. He looked at Kate with a question on his face, but she merely met his gaze blandly and looked away. She felt too exhausted to cope with anyone.

Mrs. McCormack hurried into the sunny breakfast room, looking worried.

'I don't know what you plan to do, James, but I've got the piano tuner coming, today of all days, and he'll drive you all mad.'

James smiled. 'Why we waste money having it tuned, I don't know,' he said lazily. 'No one has touched it for years.'

'It was your father's piano, James. Besides, one day you may have children who may want to—' Mrs. McCormack stopped. Her face turned an unhappy red.

'Shall we go swimming?' Kate suggested quickly. 'That would get us out of your way.'

'We could go to Komi Bay,' Mariana suggested. She looked at Randel. 'These people who swim can bathe there and we can talk.' She smiled. 'I have heard it ees very nice. There is a good restaurant, where they make delicious peri-peri chicken.'

'That's a good idea.' Mrs. McCormack sounded relieved. 'But leave me Rosa or I'll be lonely. Will you stay with me, darling?' she asked the little girl.

Rosa was drinking milk, her father, Kate noticed, watching her with a curiously thoughtful look. Rosa had a thin white moustache on her upper lip. She looked worriedly at Kate. 'If I stay, Kate, will you be all right?' she asked.

Kate felt the animosity in the quick glance Mariana gave her, and saw the annoyance on Randel's face. Kate could guess what he was thinking—that she had made Rosa dependent on her. She also saw James's amusement. Dear James—did he think Rosa felt she must protect Kate from him, lest he want revenge? Rosa knew him better than that. It was Mariana of whom she was afraid.

'I'll be quite all right, darling,' Kate said. 'And I'd hate Mrs. McCormack to feel lonely.'

'So would I,' Rosa said, and put her hand in the older woman's. 'I'd hate Mrs. McCormack to be unhappy as well as—'

Kate jumped up. Oh dear, whatever would Rosa say next? 'When shall we go?' she asked eagerly.

James planned it all, arranged everything. But at the last minute Mrs. McCormack said worriedly, 'They had sharks there, the other day.'

'We'll be careful,' James said, patting her shoulder and smiling. 'Your baby son will take care of his 'ickle self.'

His mother made a wry grimace at him and had to laugh. 'You're impossible, James. I wasn't thinking of you. It was Kate. I read about the sharks in the paper, and—'

'Well, I didn't,' James said cheerfully, 'so what I don't know about won't hurt me.' He met Kate's glance for a moment and she saw, with a shock of dismay, that he was having to make an effort to be cheerful.

'I didn't read it either,' Kate dashed into the conversation.

Mariana had turned away, as if disinterested. 'I read it. One girl was killed.'

'There!' Mrs. McCormack cried in dismay.

Randel was frowning. 'Look, please don't worry, Mrs. McCormack. There is no danger at all if one is sensible. Why on earth?' he muttered, and Kate thought he heard him mention Mariana's name. She had glided away, was now waiting with very obvious patience for the boring conversation to end. 'I promise we'll only bathe in the prescribed areas, Mrs. McCormack.'

'It's just that today I have a feeling,' she said apologetically. 'It is the thirteenth.'

Randel could smile at that. 'But that's my lucky day, which only goes to prove—'

Kate tucked her hand through the older woman's arm. 'We won't go, darling, if you're really worried.'

Mrs. McCormack smiled mistily. 'Dear girl—I don't want to spoil your fun. All the same, I'll be very glad when you're home again,' she finished defiantly.

239

CHAPTER XV

It was very pleasant at Komi Bay. Although it was crowded with visitors, there was room for all. There were specially trained life-savers, great, handsome, stalwart young men who lounged around, displaying coffee-brown suntanned biceps, the girls followed their every movement with bright eyes and eager voices. Randel, Mariana, James and Kate all swam. Someone lent them surfboards and Kate enjoyed herself, learning to come in on the great sleepy rollers, landing on the beach in a swirl of foaming water, scrambling up, shaking herself like a retriever, swimming out to try again.

It was fascinating. At first James helped her. Then he wandered over to Mariana, who was swimming with elegance and not much strength and looking bored. Kate thought with a pang of sympathy that it must be hard for James. She realised just how he felt. She had the same misery every time she saw Randel with Mariana.

Randel came up to Kate. 'I've a headache,' he said. 'I'm going up. Are you all right?'

James and Mariana were already sitting under the great beach umbrella. James was laughing. Maybe it helped him if Kate wasn't near.

'I'm fine, thanks,' she assured him. 'I'm enjoying it.'

Randel smiled. 'Good. Don't go past the flags, though.'

'Not likely!' she called gaily, as she turned to swim out. 'I'm too scared of the sharks.'

She came in after half a dozen futile attempts and had the most successful run of all. As she stood up in the foaming, swirling, lace-like water, a boy near her grinned, 'Nice work!'

Kate smiled back and turned towards the sands. She had really had enough now. She carried her board and the water was barely waist deep.

She saw something swirl by her. Something long, steel-grey and shiny—

And a voice called '*Sharks!*'

Then everything happened at once.

She turned and the shape was there again— slithering towards her. Even as she screamed, she felt something touch her leg. She stumbled forward and fell. People were screaming— falling over, bumping into her.

The water that swirled round her was red . . . Blood red.

Suddenly she found she was out of the water—being carried. Fighting waves of nausea, she stared up into Randel's face.

He held her so tightly that she could hardly breathe. He looked down at her. 'Kate—Kate!' She said sharply. 'Are you all right?'

'I don't know . . .' she said honestly. And knew no more.

Later, Mrs. McCormack told her, James had said they had just missed seeing the whole thing. They were watching her. James had just said that she had learned fast . . . and Mariana called their attention to a small boat on the horizon.

It was the sound of that fearsome cry *'Sharks!'* that made them turn.

They saw Kate falling—saw the evil grey form—saw everyone stumbling—heard the screams.

'James said Randel was down the beach like a streak of lightning and in the water,' Mrs. McCormack said. 'James followed him and Randel could hardly walk. He staggered—and you're no heavy-weight, dear child,' she smiled affectionately. That was the lovely thing about Mrs. McCormack, Kate thought. Even though she had hoped Kate would marry James and make him happy, Mrs. McCormack would never blame her, allow it to alter her affection for her.

'I wonder why he was so upset,' Kate said. 'It isn't as if it was Mariana,' she added a little bitterly.

'James says it must have been a shock. They both thought the shark had got you. The sea was full of blood.'

Kate shuddered. 'I know. I saw it. I thought it was me.'

'It was a boy, poor lamb,' Mrs. McCormack's voice thickened. 'He lost a leg.'

Kate caught her breath. 'I wonder if it was the nice kid that spoke to me . . .'

'James will know. He visits him sometimes. The boy is an orphan, was here on holiday from one of those homes. James is thinking,' Mrs. McCormack lowered her voice, '—we are thinking of adopting him. James says he is a good boy, never moans or is sorry for himself.'

'Oh, James . . .' Kate stopped herself. She did not feel she now had the right to keep saying James was *wonderful.* 'You could trust James.'

His mother nodded. 'I am blessed, aren't I?' Openly she mopped her eyes. 'Where were we, dear child?'

Kate was back at the cottage, tucked up in her own bed. She had slept solidly for two days, dosed by sedatives the doctor had ordered. Already the shock was wearing off— the tender part on her leg where the shark had scraped past her was already healing. She was enjoying being treated as an important invalid, yet getting restless.

'You said James followed Randel down to the sea,' she went on.

'Oh yes, he took you from Randel and Randel collapsed. James said it was quite extraordinary. Everyone was rushing about madly—beating off the shark—people having hysterics. Then calm came out of the chaos, he says, as an ambulance arrived. Your leg was scraped badly, but luckily not torn—of course, you were right out. Anyhow, there were nurses there and a doctor. They gave James pills for you and advised him to bring you straight home here and put you to bed. They did that, and we had the doctor. I don't expect you remember much of the rest of the day.'

'I was so drugged. It must have been shock. Mariana always said I would faint at the sight of blood,' Kate said, smiling ruefully. 'What a thing to do!'

Mrs. McCormack plumped up Kate's pillows. 'Comfortable, dear? Where was I? Oh, yes . . .' She lowered her voice and looked over her shoulder. 'You know, dear, I think Randel had a bad shock. He's so odd. He sits staring at Mariana the whole time.'

'Probably thinking how awful if it had been her,' Kate suggested.

Mrs. McCormack looked shocked. 'I suppose it could be. You know, dear child, what James told me? He said Mariana *saw* the shark. That that was the reason she called their attention to the ship. He is sure of it. She deliberately diverted their attention from you, James said.' Mrs. McCormack's whisper was horrified. 'Can you believe that any woman could be so wicked?'

Kate found herself shivering. Instinctively she caught hold of Mrs. McCormack's warm plump hand, feeling the sudden need for reassurance.

'I—think she might,' she said. She told the older woman of the scene Rosa had witnessed. 'She hit me so hard.' In memory, she touched her cheek gently. 'It was so vicious. It made me think that if she had a knife—' She shivered again.

Mrs. McCormack looked horrified. 'She must be mad. James thinks that Randel knows it, too . . . that Mariana saw the shark, I mean. That he is shocked, trying to understand that Mariana, whom he . . .'

'Worships,' Kate supplied the word, 'could be so human as to want to dispose of me.'

She saw that she had shocked Mrs. McCormack. 'I'm sorry,' she said quickly. 'But you must see that I'm standing in Mariana's way. Not really, of course, for Randel doesn't even see me as a woman—but to Mariana, I am in the way. Next time, perhaps, she won't fail.' Kate began to tremble again.

Mrs. McCormack reached for the bottle of pills. 'Oh dear, I am naughty. James would never forgive me. I've got you all upset . . .' She gave Kate a pill. 'Take this, dear, it'll make you sleep.' She hovered like an anxious mother hen. 'Oh, dear!'

Kate did not want to sleep. She wanted to think. So she pretended to meekly swallow the pill and let it slide under the bedclothes. She hazarded a guess as to the time to allow and then feigned sleepiness. She closed her eyes and felt Mrs. McCormack tucking her up, tiptoeing out of the room. Then Kate opened her eyes, looked round her and began to think.

She realised later that she must have dozed, for when she awoke it was that half-light before night. The reflection of the lights on the terrace slid into the room, making it all look unreal and very beautiful. Suddenly Kate felt very well and had the urge to see people, to talk, to return to normal life.

She stood up, surprised to find her legs a little unsteady, and pulled on her dressing-gown. She brushed back her hair; it was hot and damp and sticky from the sea water. Thrusting her feet into mules, she opened the door. Now she could see a reflection of the veranda as it showed up in the large mirror in the lounge.

Mariana, slim, lovely as ever in a gold lamé dress, was sipping a drink with an amused smile as she looked at James, and then back at Randel. Kate held the door post firmly, half wishing she was back in the safety of bed. Then she saw Mariana smile, heard that seductive husky voice say:

'But why all the fuss about her? Normal people recover from a shock—Kate was always neurotic.'

Kate moved forward, closing the door gently behind her. Now she was in the darkness with no fear of being seen. Like one hypnotised, she watched the little drama that

Kate tried to laugh. 'I'm not afraid of them, but of what they might do to Rosa. Mrs. Kelly also said she was in danger.'

A gentle cough startled them. They turned and saw Natala hesitating in the doorway. Mrs. McCormack welcomed her warmly.

'Come and sit down. This dear child works so hard, Kate, it quite worries us.' She smiled at the hesitant girl.

Natala's face glowed. 'I would kill myself with work to please Senhor James,' she declared.

'That wouldn't help him much,' Mrs. McCormack said dryly, and then smiled. But her eyes, as they met Kate's, held a question. Kate wished they were alone so that she could reassure her friend. Mrs. McCormack need not fear Natala was falling in love with James; Antonio's slim, olive-skinned fingers held Natala's heart firmly in their grasp.

Natala said, 'I am so happy Rosa is safe, but so afraid for you, *Kett.* You may say I am being mello . . . mello . . .' She shook her head, searching for the word. '—Melodramatic, but do you not see your danger? All these years, the Senhor Lister has paid for the ménage of the Dominguez. That has been of use, for they had nothing, but nothing.' She saw their surprised faces. 'Ah—there are many stories told of the Dominguez in this town and none of them are pretty. Desperate, they were lucky to have the Senhor to come to their aid.'

207

showed so clearly in the mirror.

James was moving, refilling glasses. Randel was sitting, slumped in a chair, looking at Mariana as if he wanted to eat her.

Kate's heart seemed to skid. She turned away. Why torture herself?

Then James's words gripped her attention. He handed the glass to Mariana and spoke to Randel. 'I've just heard about that Fortescue case, Lister. Bad luck on them, isn't it? But they ought to have used their brains, if they have any.'

Randel moved his head slowly. He was a changed man. Kate's heart cried out in pain, What has happened? Don't, please don't look like that.

'I don't remember.'

'Tell me, James—my James,' Mariana said gaily.

James came to sit near her, smiling at her. 'Just bad luck on a couple who are desperately in love and now find they can't marry.'

A strange cautious look crossed Mariana's face. 'Why not?'

He turned away, flicked the ash off his cigarette. 'She was brought up as an orphan. Has just discovered her real parents. Now she finds that her husband-to-be is the widower of her sister.' He burst out laughing, but the others did not join in. Randel went on staring moodily at Mariana and Mariana frowned.

'I do not understand.'

'I don't expect you do,' James said cheerfully. 'Boiled down to plain English it's this—by English law, a man cannot marry his widow's sister.'

'She can't?' Mariana said slowly.

'No, she can't,' James said, grinning. He stood up, went to the window and fastened the mosquito netting. 'Pity, but there it is. It is the law.' He came back, looked at Randel. 'Drink up, old man.'

Randel looked up and seemed to come out of a dream. 'You know, James, I thought that law had been passed,' he remarked.

Kate, standing very still, leaning against the cold wall, watched them. She saw Mariana's quick look at the two men, saw the way she pretended to be interested in the glass in her hand. Saw James look at Randel—and, despite the distance, saw him wink.

'What? Oh!' Randel said in some confusion. 'They're trying to get it passed, are they?' He looked so confused that Kate longed to rush in and comfort him. But he would not want comfort from her . . .

To Kate's dismay, James murmured some excuse and walked right down the corridor. He had obviously seen her, for he grinned and came to stand by her side, taking her weight on his arm which went right round her.

'Keep still, I've laid a trap. Trouble is, Lister's behaving very oddly and I wonder if he's got the sense to make use of it,' he

248

whispered.

Mariana was standing up, moving round the room, turning out the lamps. Now they could only see her faintly—but they could hear her voice.

'Randel, my Randel—what is wrong? You are angry with me.'

They guessed she was sitting on the arm of his chair. Kate closed her eyes, imagining that long, cool, lovely hand stroking back the hair from Randel's head.

'Randel, tell me the truth, my darling. Is that why we are not married? Because I am your late wife's sister?'

There was silence. Kate felt James's body tense against her, his hand tighten on hers.

'What reason?' Randel asked dully.

Kate felt James sigh, heard him whisper, 'What's wrong with the man?'

'Oh, my Randel, you heard what James said. That a man cannot marry his widow's sister. Is that why you cannot marry me?'

'Look, Mariana—' Randel sounded beyond help, so utterly tired. 'Why must we go over this again? James has told you—'

'So!' Her voice changed, became low, soft, pleading.

'You love me, Randel, that I know. That everyone knows. They see it when you look at me, hear it in your voice. They wonder at the delay. Now that I know, we can put the matter right. All will be well—we can find happiness.'

Her voice soared triumphantly.

'What are you talking about?' Randel said. Kate jumped a little. He sounded irritable, impatient. With Mariana?

'My Randel, I have a secret to tell you. Swear you will forgive. Swear you forgive, my Randel.'

'The needle seems to have got stuck in the groove,' James whispered wickedly in Kate's ear. She turned to look at him in the dimness, half shocked, half amused. 'I'm afraid poor Randel is missing his cues.'

'What is it, Mariana?' Randel said, and it was the voice Kate knew so well—tolerant, forgiving, patient.

'Randel,' Mariana was now using her most dramatic tone. 'I am not your wife's sister.'

'What!' In the mirror, they could see he had stood up. That now Mariana was standing too, facing him, hands clasped, face lifted imploringly.

'Do not be angry, my Randel,' she said quickly. 'We were desperate—starving. We heard of the death, and my mother thought we could help. You took it for granted that we were her mother and sister.' She caught his arm.

'You told me you were,' Randel exclaimed.

'Only afterwards. It was tempting to agree. We were starving,' she pleaded.

Kate felt James's hand behind her, felt him turn the knob that touched her back, push open the door and lead her inside. He left her by the bed.

'We're best out of this,' he said. 'Randel can handle it now.'

'Oh, James, if he knew you!' Kate breathed. Poor Randel—now he knew that his beloved was a liar, a cheat . . .

James touched her arm lightly. 'Hop into bed and I'll send along some dinner. Mother has retired to bed with a headache.'

'Your poor mother!'

James bent and kissed the tip of her nose lightly. 'The same old Kate,' he said gently. 'Unfortunately,' he added, and left her.

Kate lay in bed, longing to know what was happening, yearning over Randel. How terrible for him! So Natala's story was true. She must write to Natala, already on her way to America and good health. And romance, for James had told Kate that he was giving Natala a very substantial 'dowry' and that would fix Antonio, all right. James seemed to think that, with Natala behind him, Antonio might turn out all right. James was a sort of fairy godfather, wasn't he, Kate thought. If only he could meet the right person! He deserved to be happy. And then she thought of Randel Lister again, and could have wept with sympathy for him.

In the morning Mrs. McCormack announced with glee that Mariana had already left, and Randel was going that afternoon.

251

'He says you and Rosa can stay another month and then he will make arrangements. I think he will take a villa. My dear . . .' she lowered her voice, 'James tells me that dreadful story about the Dominguez was true. What a couple!'

'I'm sorry for Randel—it must be awful to be disillusioned,' Kate said.

'I think you're being sorry for the wrong person,' Mrs. McCormack said, in an unusually tart voice.

'Where is Rosa?' Kate asked.

Mrs. McCormack looked vague. 'Around somewhere. Do you want her?'

'No.' Kate watched the door close as she was left alone. Why wouldn't they let her get up? Would Randel go off without even seeing her? How could she bear it?

She turned her face to the pillow and the tears rolled down her cheeks. She hated herself for crying. Why was she so weak? Mariana was right—she was weak . . .

'Kate!' Randel's voice said quietly.

Kate turned round, and he was standing there. He looked ill at ease. Well, most men were unhappy in a sickroom, though this shouldn't be considered a sickroom, for they were just spoiling her. Or keeping her prisoner? Had Randel said he did not want to see her? If so, why was he here? These thoughts whirled in her mind as she stared at him.

He came forward and, with an oddly abashed gesture, gave her a spray of roses. 'Rosa and I picked them,' he told her.

Kate stared at him. It was the first time he had ever called Rose Rosa.

'How is she?' she asked.

He sat down. 'Worried about you.'

Kate swallowed. 'I don't know why she should be worried . . .'

He smiled—that same thrilling, never-to-be-forgotten smile. Kate felt the old magic again and her mouth was dry.

'Kate,' he said, and took her hand gently. 'Kate—is it true?'

She could hardly speak. 'Is what true?'

'What Rosa tells me. That I am the only man in the world you would marry?'

If ever she had prayed for the ground to open up and swallow her, it was now. She could not answer—could only stare at him, hypnotised by shock and embarrassment. But Randel did not wait for an answer. He hitched his chair closer to the bed, put both hands on her limp one and went on.

'If so, I'll be the happiest man in the whole world. I was sure you hated me, despised me. Oh, Kate!' he said, with an impulsiveness she had never seen in him before. 'I've behaved just like a crazy mixed-up kid.' He smiled, tried to laugh. 'Oh, Kate, how could I have been so blind? So bewitched? There is no excuse. I honestly thought Rosa was being looked after kindly—that they loved her, that I owed them gratitude. Now I find they were frauds—that it was a plot. But they *did* look after her—but in what a way! I've been so selfish—so—stupid.' He smiled ruefully. 'Kate, right from the beginning I've wronged you, distrusted you, never given you a chance. I wouldn't blame you if you despised me. I thought you loved James—I knew he loved you. I thought when you left me, you would marry him. I still thought it—until just now.'

She sat very still, just staring at him. Soon, she thought, she would wake up, find it one of her dreams . . .

'Just now I asked Rosa what we would do when you got married. She said you would live with us, of course. I said how could that be— and she told me that you said . . .' His voice faltered. 'Did you say that, Kate? Did you mean it?'

Kate found her voice. She had thought it would be a tiny squeak. Instead it was almost a shout—'Yes!'

And then there was no need for words. He scooped her up in his arms and was kissing her—her mouth, her throat, her eyes. Murmuring all the wonderful words she had not dared put in her dreams, because somehow she could never picture Randel using them.

But he was . . . he was telling her he adored her. Making plans for them—calling her his beautiful—his beloved—

He stopped for a second to get his breath. He smiled at her. 'My darling!' he said softly.

The door opened and there was Rosa, her face cautious. When she saw Kate in her father's arms she ran across the room.

Her father opened his arms, so that now he could hold the two of them close to his heart.

Rosa looked at Kate. 'Well?' she asked.

Kate smiled. 'It is *well*—darling. Very well, indeed,' she said, and bent and kissed the child.